TAKING CARE OF SAFETY

Other books in this series

Looking After Corporate Health
John Humphrey and Paul Smith

Making Equal Opportunities Work
Mary Coussey and Hilary Jackson

PERSONNEL
Today

TAKING CARE OF SAFETY

R A Saunders

Pitman Publishing
128 Long Acre, London WC2E 9AN

A Division of Longman Group UK Limited

First published in 1992

© Longman Group UK Ltd 1992

British Library Cataloguing in Publication Data

Saunders, R.A.
  Taking care of safety. — (Personnel today series)
  I. Title II. Series
  658.3

ISBN 0 273 03507 X

Printed in Great Britain by The Bath Press, Avon

To Richard, Rebecca and Timothy

Contents

Civil liability · Discipline · Reasonable care and the breach
of duty · Burden of proof · Employers have a common law
duty of care · The duty to provide competent staff · The
duty to provide adequate material, premises and plant · The
duty to provide a proper system and effective
supervision · Vicarious liability · Contributory
negligence · Implications of the common law for the
management of an effective safety campaign · Common law
duties to non-employees · Division of control · **Criminal
liability** · Statutory duties of employers · General duties of
employers · Statutory duties to non-employees · Hybrid
offences · Other forms of guidance · **Health and Safety at
Work Act 1974** · Implications of the Act · Safety
representatives and committees · **Enforcement of the
health and safety provisions** · Enforcement notices ·
Prosecution · Aspects of personal liability ·
Managerial responsibility · Employee motivation · Selection
of contractors · **Some relevant Acts of Parliament** ·
Employers' Liability (defective equipment) Act 1969 ·
Employers' Liability (compulsory insurance) Act 1969 ·
Occupiers' Liability Act 1959 · Congenital Disabilities
(civil liability) Act 1976 · Fatal Accidents Act 1976 · Law
Reform (miscellaneous provisions) Act 1934 ·
Limitations Act 1975 · **Regulations** · Approved codes
of practice · Assessing what is reasonably
practicable · **The Council of the European
Communities** · Summary · **Checklist**

vibration · **Radiation – VDUs** · **Protective clothing** · **Manual handling** · Transport · Stacking and storing · **Lifting equipment** · **Dangerous substances and the control of substances hazardous to health (COSHH)** · How can substances hazardous to health be identified · Observe, find out and consider · Action to be taken · **Welfare** · **Alcohol and drugs** · **Stress management** · **Cleaning** · Hygiene · **Checklist**

Foreword

People are central to the success of every business; they are the only source of sustainable competitive advantage. Companies which succeed have positive well-established policies for managing them.

Managers must take the lead in creating an environment where the full potential of every employee can be realised and rewarded.

The creation of a flexible, motivated workforce involves providing opportunities at all levels and in all functions, under-pinned by an equal opportunities policy. This benefits individuals and businesses and makes the best use of the skills and talents of the workforce.

The environment in which people work is of fundamental importance. Healthy and safe working surroundings mean high quality standards of protection and performance and ensure the well-being of all those in the workplace.

In addition corporate healthcare encourages healthy work and lifestyle practices. Not only are these beneficial for the individual but also contribute to lower absenteeism, improved performance and higher morale. Sickness absence alone costs British business well over £5 billion a year.

These comprehensive, practical books use the examples of a large number of companies and are designed for day-to-day use by personnel managers. Each book considers the value of the programmes, benefits to be gained, practical implementation and the costs involved.

John Banham,
Director-General,
Confederation of British Industry.

Foreword

I have the privilege of overviewing the safety programmes and perform-
ances of many companies – from the largest to the smallest – in 24
different countries, and whilst I recommend the employment of a good
Safety Officer/Manager, I am heartened that companies without such,
but with effective Personnel Officers, often have very good safety
records.

I am therefore very pleased that *Taking Care of Safety*, aimed specifically at Personnel Officers and Managers, is to be published in the
Personnel Today series. It has been said many times that we are living
in an information explosion age, and that certainly applies in the
Occupational Health and Safety field. The British Safety Council is an
official consulting body, yet we can barely keep pace with the European
Directives, let alone the several hundred European Standards.

Indeed, the training of safety professionals nowadays has moved away
from the accumulation of data (which can easily be referred to on computers) towards knowing where to look for information, and this is
fully dealt with in the book.

Ninety per cent of the time, when I am visiting the scene of an accident, I find myself saying 'But the man wasn't trained', which is, of
course, why we put so much emphasis on good training. I am therefore
delighted with the chapters that cover training objectives through to
a final check-list.

You will, of course, know that the Health and Safety Commission
in their Plan of Work recommend audit systems, and that the HSE
direct Inspectors to recommend Management Audit Systems such as
our Five Star System. Effective bodies are already using Management
Audit Systems in order to measure safety performance before an accident, and I am pleased to see that this subject is also covered in this
really valuable publication.

If you employ a Safety Officer/Adviser then this publication would provide a useful check on what the job should involve; if you have not employed a Safety Officer, then this little information-packed book is a *must* on your desk.

James Tye
Director General
British Safety Council

CHAPTER 1
Health and Safety Legislation

In this chapter we shall be dealing with civil and criminal liability, the Health and Safety at Work Act 1974 and Health and Safety enforcement. Some relevant Acts of Parliament will be looked at together with regulations in force and the role of the Council for European Communities.

Personnel managers with a responsibility for health and safety have a major role within their organisation for ensuring that appropriate safety systems are in force and that they comply with the law. They must also ensure that statutory regulations are obeyed. Their role will be to ensure that both the general policy and strategic decisions relating to safety are in place. It is essential that these are translated on a daily basis into detailed plans and procedures for staff to follow. Finally, the personnel manager must insist that these systems operate effectively without any lapses. Generally, the law requires the manager to ensure that safe systems exist within the organisation; that there is effective maintenance of both buildings and equipment; that staff have received appropriate and adequate safety training, information about health and safety procedures and practice, instruction about safe practices and policies, and proper supervision when undertaking hazardous or dangerous activities; the safety of others, including the general public who may be affected by operations of the organisation; and that third parties such as contractors or consultants hired by the organisation do not endanger staff nor are endangered by them.

Failure to comply with these requirements will almost certainly result in the prosecution of your organisation and in certain circumstances you can be held *personally* liable for both criminal and civil proceedings.

In this chapter we will simply be summarising the rather complex subject of health and safety law, tracing the legal developments of particular interest to personnel managers. For those who require more detailed information on the law, a reading list is given at the end of the chapter.

Enforcement strategies operating within the legal framework impinge on those responsible for safety, particularly when things go wrong. It is the responsibility of the manager, in this case the personnel manager, to be aware when plans under discussion need expert advice and to seek it from qualified legal staff or appropriate technical consultancies. Personnel officers with responsibility for health and safety matters will therefore need to be kept up-to-date with legislative improvements and changes, and membership of one or more of those organisations listed in the Appendix is highly recommended.

When examining safety-related case law, it can be concluded that it has largely been established as the result of the safety management system failing to meet the aims and objectives of the organisation. It is axiomatic that companies do not maliciously set out to injure their workforce, but there are many examples where 'other factors', usually of a financial nature, have compromised the need for an effective safety policy. In such instances, it would seem that safety is often regarded as a worthwhile priority by an organisation until a conflict arises between safety and the balance sheet. Safety management should be seen in terms of *profit* rather than *expense*. To illustrate this it will be necessary to acquaint the reader with some of the relevant issues regarding safety and the law from a personnel management standpoint.

Throughout the book, any reference to safety will include all health issues and any other areas which are hazardous or dangerous in the workplace.

Civil liability

Common law is a part of the English legal system which is regarded to be traditional and is effective in areas not covered by Act of Parliament. The principles and rules of common law are contained in those decisions taken previously in English courts. They are recorded in the law reports and go back to the Middle Ages. Health and safety issues started to appear in case law during the industrial revolution when casualties began to sue for compensation following injuries received at work. Common law is based on what has been decided before by judges and is referred to as precedent. Although there are a few technical exceptions, a court is bound to follow those decisions made earlier in courts of equal or higher status, unless statute law dictates to the contrary. Common law governs the rights and duties of individuals towards one another.

Generally, there are four types of remedies available to an individual.

- **Compensation** A cash value is placed upon the injury suffered or the loss experienced where an employer is found to be liable through failure to comply with the law.
- **Reparation** Where an employer is required to restore conditions so that they are the same as before the breach of the law.
- **Performance** Where an employer can be compelled to perform their obligations.
- **Injunction** Where an employer can be required to desist from an activity where it interferes with the common law rights of another.

Civil actions can be initiated in a variety of courts. In order of increasing seniority, they are as follows.

- **County court** Inexpensive, relatively fast. A single circuit judge can award damages up to £5,000.
- **High Court (Queen's Bench Division)** Expensive, relatively slow. Single judge can award unlimited damages.
- **Court of Appeal** Very expensive, can be relatively quick. Typically, three senior judges have the power to hear appeals from the High Court, county courts and tribunals, and can uphold, amend or reverse the decision of a lower court.

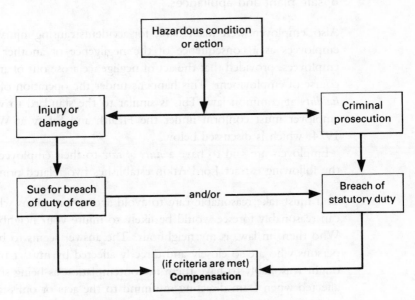

Figure 1.1 Courses of action in a claim for compensation

HEALTH AND SAFETY LEGISLATION

- **House of Lords** Extremely expensive and slow. Three of the most senior judges constitute this, the final court of appeal within the UK.
- **European Court** It can potentially cause a case to be reviewed where interpretation is needed about an EC Directive on domestic law in the field of health and safety.

It is said that common law can be traced back a thousand years although matters referring to safety matters began appearing in the mid-19th century. This coincided with the industrial revolution and the advent of the factory. Under common law, workers could sue their employers in the courts for compensation for injuries received while at work. Common law requires that an employer must take reasonable care to protect his employees from risk of foreseeable injury, disease or death at work. In the 19th and early part of the 20th century, employers argued with reasonable degrees of success against this duty in respect of proving the 'foreseeable' aspect of the law. It was not until 1938 in *Wilsons & Clyde Coal Co Ltd v English* [1938] AC 57, that the House of Lords identified, in general terms, the duties of an employer at common law. They judged that all employers are required to provide and maintain:

- a safe place of work;
- a competent staff of men (or women);
- a safe system of work;
- safe plant and appliances.

Also, employers were made liable for accidents causing injury to their employees as a consequence of the negligence of another of their employees, provided that the act of negligence arose out of and in the course of employment. This happens under the operation of *vicarious liability* at common law. This is similar to the standard to which an employer must conform under the Health and Safety at Work Act 1974, which is discussed below.

Employers are said to have a *duty of care* to their employees and in the following extract Lord Atkin establishes two related principles:

You must take reasonable care to avoid acts or omissions which you can reasonably foresee would be likely to injure your neighbour. Who then, in law, is my neighbour? The answer seems to be persons who are so closely and directly affected by my act that I ought reasonably to have them in contemplation as being so affected when I am directing my mind to the acts or omissions which are called in question.

DONOGHUE V STEVENSON

An important and influential case which established important precedents for health and safety was that of *Donoghue v Stevenson* [1932] AC 562. The judges' findings were to apply to all industries in the future. Stevenson, the defendant, manufactured ginger beer which was put into opaque bottles before sale. R, a retailer, sold the ginger beer to C and he gave a bottle to a friend Donoghue, the plaintiff. Donoghue complained that the bottle contained the decomposed remains of a snail. As a result, Donoghue was ill from drinking the contents of the bottle. Donoghue had no contract with Stevenson on which liability could be based. The legal question was whether there was any other basis of liability. The House of Lords found by a three to two majority that there was. The principle can be found in the words of Lord Atkin:

A manufacturer of products, which he sells in such a form as to show that he intends them to reach the ultimate consumer in the form in which they left him with no reasonable possibility of intermediate examination, and with the knowledge that the absence of reasonable care in the preparation or putting up of the products will result in an injury to the consumer's life or property, owes a duty to the consumer to take that reasonable care.

This principle was later to influence judges in other cases as will be seen below. Although here it was specifically health that was at issue, the principle established can be seen to influence both the health and safety aspects of an organisation.

BOURHILL (OR HAY) V YOUNG

The 'neighbour principle' has been defined in a number of cases, for example in *Bourhill (or Hay) v Young* [1943] AC 92. Young was a motorcyclist who, because of his careless driving, was killed in a collision with a car. Bourhill, who was pregnant, heard the collision from a distance and on approaching the scene of the accident saw blood in the road. This caused her nervous shock and as a consequence she subsequently gave birth to a stillborn child. Bourhill sued Young's representatives. She failed in her case because it was held that Young could not reasonably be expected to foresee injury to a person as far from the accident as the plaintiff had been at the time of the collision. Thus, Bourhill was not Young's 'neighbour' and was owed no duty of care.

KING V PHILLIPS

In *King v Phillips* [1953] 1 QB 429, a careless taxi-driver reversed over a child's tricycle in the road occasioning the child to scream. The child's mother, thinking that her child had been killed, suffered nervous shock and became ill. King sued the taxi-driver. It was held that Phillips owed only a duty of care to such persons as he could reasonably foresee might be injured by his actions in the immediate vicinity of his vehicle. As King had been in a house nearby, she was not Phillips's neighbour and was again owed no duty of care.

DOUGHTY V TURNER MANUFACTURING CO LTD

When assessing reasonably foreseeable risks at work, the employer's actual or imputed knowledge of the risks is most important. As a personnel manager responsible for safety matters you will be held liable for your own actions and those of your subordinates with regard to communicating or otherwise acting on complaints from employees or other sources of information.

In *Doughty v Turner Manufacturing Co Ltd* [1964] 1 QB 518, a fellow worker of Doughty let an asbestos cement cover fall into a cauldron of molten metal which resulted in an explosion causing an injury to Doughty. No similar accidents of this kind had occurred previously and it was not known that explosions were caused by asbestos cement mixing with molten metal. Although the action of the defendant's servant was the direct cause of the accident, it could not be shown that the defendant had failed to exercise reasonable foresight. Thus the defendant was not liable.

ROWARK V NATIONAL COAL BOARD

In *Rowark v National Coal Board* [1986] unreported 86/45 CA, R, a miner, was involved in hauling half-ton wagons of waste materials along a 400 yard stretch of rail track. He was engaged on this work for a period of three months. As a result, he developed tenosynovitis, a painful inflammation of the wrist tendons. He claimed damages. The employer's defence was that this specific condition could not have been foreseen as a consequence of this kind of work. Here the decision concerned whether the injury was reasonably foreseeable. It was not necessary for the specific type of injury to be foreseen. In this particular case, some kind of strain to the wrists was foreseeable to a person expected to push such heavy loads over a prolonged period of time. Here, there was a breach of duty to provide a powered haulage system. May LJ stated that:

The precise nature of the injury does not need to be foreseen if its general nature can; and the fact that tenosynovitis is an inflammation of the tendon or sheath is not sufficient to categorise it as a kind which is not foreseeable, whereas strains or sprains and the like are.

STOKES V GUEST, KEEN & NETTLEFOLD (BOLTS & NUTS) LTD

It has been said that an employer has a duty to take reasonable care for the safety of their employees acting in the course of their employment. Under common law, there is no liability without proof of negligence. The duty is to take reasonable care, not guarantee the employees' safety. If the employer can show that they have taken reasonable care then the employee's claim under this head will fail despite the seriousness of any injuries which may have been received. This general duty to take reasonable care is well illustrated in *Stokes v Guest, Keen & Nettlefold (Bolts & Nuts) Ltd* [1968] 1 WLR 1776.

Stokes had been employed by GKN for 15 years as a toolsetter. He died of scrotal cancer in 1966. His work involved leaning over machines in such a way as to bring the lower part of his body and upper thighs into contact with cutting oil. As a result his clothes became saturated with the oil which resulted in the skin of the groin being frequently smothered in lubricant. This undoubtedly caused the cancer and his subsequent death.

The standard to apply here, and in all matters of 'negligence' was that of a reasonable and prudent employer who adopts a positive attitude towards safety in the light of what is known and what should be known. It is right to assume that an employer will keep abreast of new developments and knowledge, and must be ready to use and apply them. However, the duty of care does not necessarily require a person to have done everything possible to prevent an accident resulting in injury. On the contrary, risk must be assessed and one has to consider the likelihood of an accident happening and be aware of the consequences. From this, a person may balance the effectiveness of precautions or preventative methods against the expense and any inconvenience of taking them. In *Stokes*, the court found that the work could not reasonably have been organised or the machines modified to obviate the regular contact with the oil. Also, the plaintiff did not argue that any less potentially carcinogenic oil was commercially available (though failure to investigate that possibility could, in other circumstances, constitute negligence). In addition, the plaintiff did not argue that it was unreasonable to carry on his work in the circumstances described. But did the defendants act reasonably in respect of protective clothing?

The court found that the only clothing available at the time was unpopular, hot and very cumbersome. The important point here is Stokes's reluctance to wear the clothing. If an employee claims that the employer was negligent in failing to provide protective clothing, but the employer can demonstrate that if they had it would not have been worn anyway, the action will fail because the injury could not have been caused by the employers but the employee's omission. This raises a valid point in questioning how far an employer should go in making their workforce wear protective clothing.

There is no clear answer and the particular circumstances will decide the issue. For example, if the employee is highly experienced at his or her job and is fully aware of the dangers inherent in carrying out the work, it might be considered satisfactory to advertise the availability of protective clothing and do no more. However, if the employee was also young and inexperienced the employer would need to do much more.

In *Stokes*, the judge was satisfied with safety standards within GKN. There was a full-time medical officer employed with qualified assistants and a well equipped surgery. Washing facilities were available and a scheme for cleaning overalls was provided. A safety officer was on the staff. Despite all this, the main argument against GKN was about its failure to warn and/or instruct the deceased about the dangers to which he was exposed. Information about the precautions he should have taken were lacking and regular medical examinations of high risk toolsetters were not carried out. When questioned on this by the company, the medical officer, who was well aware of the risks, advised management to the contrary. This was because the doctor felt that the time spent examining employees far outweighed the risks involved. The court felt that the medical officer exaggerated this claim. The problem could have been rectified with the employment of additional staff but the doctor was reluctant to do this because management were not supportive of such suggestions. The court heard of a similar case in 1963 involving another toolsetter dying from scrotal cancer, yet still the doctor did not consider regular medical examinations to be important. As is usual with fatalities, details of the case became known via a variety of ways to other workers in the factory. The judge commented harshly on the unsatisfactory way in which staff learnt of this type of danger. He was also critical of management because they had not obtained and circulated a leaflet produced by the factory inspectorate on this subject.

The court applied the 'test of the prudent employer' and found that there was negligence on the part of GKN in:

- not instituting periodical medical examinations after the first death in 1963, and
- not issuing the factory inspectorate leaflet available on the matter.

It was deemed that these steps could have saved the life of Stokes and damages of £10,000 were awarded.

This particular case illustrates a break-down in the safety management processes within the workplace and the importance of safety managers having authority within an organisation in order to maximise the efficiency and effectiveness of safety policies and programmes. It is wrong to employ a safety expert on the one hand, and on the other to override his or her advice. Being aware of how the law views certain matters is important. A case which might appear before a judge concerning a particular industry may have far-reaching implications for all industries and not just the one under discussion in court.

DAVIE V NEW MERTON BOARD MILLS LTD

In 1959, the case of *Davie v New Merton Board Mills Ltd* [1959] AC 604 was heard, where New Merton Board Mills, the employer, bought a number of drifts (a tool made up of a bar of tapered steel measuring approximately 1-foot long) from a reputable supplier, B. When Davie, an employee, was using one of the drifts in the correct manner, a splinter shot off and caught him in the eye. This resulted in Davie losing the sight in this eye. From an examination of the tool, the steel used was excessively hard because of the negligence of G during manufacture. G was liable to Davie on the *Donoghue v Stevenson* principle discussed above. It was found that New Merton Board Mills had purchased from a reputable supplier, that the drift was in good condition and that New Merton Board Mills's system of maintenance was not negligent. It was deemed unreasonable to expect an employer to test a drift for hardness before issuing it to an employee. This problem could not reasonably have been noticed without submitting the drift to such a test. New Merton Board Mills was deemed to have taken reasonable care and was found not liable.

The case highlighted a weakness not in New Merton Board Mills's system but in that of B. In this case B should have examined its quality control methods to identify how this problem occurred and to take all reasonable steps to prevent it happening again. These would be regarded as environmental investigations and should be supervised by the manager responsible for safety.

SMITH V SCOTT BOWYERS LTD

However, an employer's negligence may lie in failure to take reasonable care to ensure that a place of work is safe as this case illustrates. In *Smith v. Scott Bowyers Ltd* [1986] IRLR 315, Smith worked in a food factory where the floor was always wet and greasy. In order to protect employees from the slippery conditions, the employer provided special waterproof boots that had a diamond grip anti-slip sole. When the soles wore smooth, replacements were available on demand. It was the responsibility of employees to ask for them and to keep an eye on the condition of their boots. No steps were taken by the employer to check on the state of employees' boots or to exhort them to check their own boots. Normally, Smith had asked for replacement boots when they had worn smooth but on this occasion had not done so and had slipped. He claimed damages for his injuries. The High Court awarded damages because of the employer's failure to exhort employees to use safety equipment. However, the Court of Appeal reversed this decision and found that the employer was not at fault.

Here the appeal judges found that this was a clear case of a simple, readily understood risk against which the employer had made adequate safety equipment provision. In such a case, it is the duty of an employee to protect him or her self as discussed in *Qualcast Ltd v Haynes* below.

QUALCAST (WOLVERHAMPTON) LTD V HAYNES

In *Qualcast (Wolverhampton) Ltd v Haynes* (1959) 2 All ER 38, HL, Haynes was an experienced foundryman. While pouring molten metal from a hand-held ladle some molten metal splashed on to his foot. He was not wearing heavy boots or leather spats, although both were readily available from company stores. His foot was injured and he claimed damages for the employer's failure to encourage him to wear spats. Here there was no overriding rule that an employer must provide any safety equipment or exhort men to use it. While the duty of care to employees remains the same, the practical steps the employer takes to prevent injury will vary according to the gravity of the risk and the experience of the individual employer.

Where risks of serious injury are not great and an employee has sufficient experience to know the risks well, the employer's duty is discharged when they make safety equipment available and leave the decision whether to use them or not with experienced workers. Lord Radcliffe stated:

There may be cases in which an employer does not discharge his duty of care towards his workmen merely by providing an article of safety equipment, but courts should be circumspect in filling out that duty with the much vaguer obligation of encouraging, exhorting or instructing workmen or a particular workman to make regular use of what is provided.

Where accepted practice can normally be used in defence, the duty of care extends to the employer to consider whether the practice is adequate and whether or not there is a need to change it. Some cases highlight a reactive management strategy whereby no action is taken until the law provides for it. Such management strategies are open to action of this nature, particularly if an organisation chooses to allow courts of law to make their safety management decisions. An over-enthusiastic safety policy can close most factories by making them too safe. In this instance, it can be said that a workplace can only be deemed to be completely safe when it is shut! Risks have to be accepted, so it is essential that safety management should be proactive by nature. Risk analysis and a historical accident and dangerous occurrence database are prerequisites. A court is influenced if safety management decisions are made for sound reasons. Management strategies that are incompetent are easily shown to be negligent by courts as can be seen above.

Discipline

While the requirements of the law are being discussed, there is one aspect of the enforcement strategy which is important to consider here. This is in the area of discipline. Many safety practitioners need to appreciate that the enforcement strategy includes the safety rules which operate within an organisation. Breaches of discipline must be dealt with quickly and fairly. If an employee is in breach of a rule or rules then a fair system for dealing with this must be established. The ultimate disciplinary action here would be dismissal.

HUDSON V. RIDGE MANUFACTURING

In law, the duty of care may require an employer to discipline or even dismiss an employee who is a source of danger to his or her workmates. This was proven in *Hudson v Ridge Manufacturing* [1957] 2 QB 348, where an employee continually took part in dangerous horseplay against his work mates. Despite several reprimands from his foreman to desist, a worker was eventually injured as a result of the skylarking. The company was held liable, since reprimands are not enough. Another implication of this will be discussed below.

Reasonable care and the breach of duty

The test of reasonable care is determined by a court on the basis of what a reasonable person would do in the same circumstances as the defendant. If the existence of the duty of care is established as a matter of law then the breach of this duty is decided by the judge.

LATIMER V AEC LTD

In *Latimer v AEC Ltd* [1953] AC 643, a very heavy rainfall flooded the defendant's workshops and caused oil to spread over the floors where it remained in patches. The defendant immediately sent men to clean the floor and cover any oil patches with sawdust. There was insufficient sawdust and some oily patches were left uncovered. Latimer slipped on one of these patches, broke his leg and sued his employers. Where an employer fails in his duty and an employee is injured the employer will be held to be negligent. The employer must just take reasonable care not to subject his employees to unnecessary risk.

Despite Latimer showing cause and effect, directness, foresight and a duty of care, the defendants were held not to be liable because their only alternative was to close the factory which would have been unreasonable. The degree of care, the amount of effort required and the cost to the employer will depend chiefly on the magnitude of the risk.

EDWARDS V NCB

In *Edwards v NCB* [1949] 1 KB 704, Asquith LJ stated that 'a computation must be made in which the quantum of risk is placed on one scale, and the sacrifice involved in the measures necessary for averting the risk is placed on the other'. The more probable an accident is, the greater is the duty to guard against it. Even if the probability is quite small, but the magnitude of risk in terms of serious potential injury is great, stringent precautions will be necessary.

There are five factors to consider when determining reasonable care.

1. **Cost** The amount of money that it is necessary to spend against a slight possibility of risk is limited.
2. **Obviousness of risk** The more obvious the danger the more likely it is that the employer will be held liable for failing to prevent an accident. A partial defence to this is that the employee may have been aware of the risk, in which case there is held to be contributory negligence.
3. **Inherent risk** All work carries with it some possibility of risk

which is irreducible or irremovable and for which the employer cannot be held responsible.

4. **Likelihood of injury** 'The greater the risk, the greater the liability.'
5. **Seriousness of injury** 'The more serious the consequences, the more precautions should have been taken.'

Burden of proof

'He who asserts must prove.' Generally, the plaintiff must prove that the action or omission of the defendant actually caused the injury. However, the rule of *res ipsa loquitur* (the thing speaks for itself) assumes that the only possible explanation for the injury was the defendant's negligence. Here the onus is on the defendant to prove that this was not the case.

The plaintiff is required to demonstrate

- **cause and effect** In other words that the defendant's negligent act or omission caused the injury or loss;
- **alternative** the plaintiff must show that there was a reasonable alternative open to the defendant which, if taken, would have prevented the injury or loss;
- **foresight** the plaintiff has to demonstrate that the defendant should have known of the risk;
- **Directness** in the *Smith v Leech Braine & Co Ltd* [1962] 2 QB 405 case the principle that the defendant is liable for all damage, whether foreseeable or not, which is a direct consequence of his act or omission is established. Here, molten zinc flew out of a galvanising tank causing a burn to the lip of Smith, an employee. Subsequently, cancer developed on the site of the burn which resulted in the man's death. The widow sued here husband's former employer. It was held that the defendants were liable, even though the death could not have been foreseeable as a result of the accident.

McWILLIAMS (OR CUMMINGS) V SIR WILLIAM ARROL & CO

In *McWilliams (or Cummings) v Sir William Arrol & Co* [1962] 1 WLR 295, a steel erector fell 70 feet and was killed. Evidence showed that a safety belt would have prevented the fall, but that even if it had been provided it would not have been worn. It was held by the House of Lords that the failure to provide equipment was not the cause of the damage.

PARIS V STEPNEY COUNCIL

However, in *Paris v Stepney Council* [1951] AC 367, it was held that goggles were thought necessary for an employee known by his employers to have only one eye, though not for other employees doing the same work. Although the likelihood of injury to his remaining good eye was slight, the consequences for Paris were clearly serious since the accident resulted in total blindness. Where an employer knows that an employee is disabled or is particularly at risk, a greater duty of care is owed to these employees, compared to that afforded to normal, healthy employees with no disability.

RE POLEMIS V FURNESS WITHY & CO

The principle of directness was upheld in *Re Polemis v Furness Withy & Co* [1921] 3 KB 560. Stevedores, employed by charterers of a ship, negligently caused a plank to fall into the hold of a ship containing flammable vapour. The resulting spark caused a fire which destroyed the ship. Although some damage to the ship could be foreseen, the sparks could not have been foreseen. The charterers were held liable for the ship's loss as this was a direct, although not foreseeable, consequence of the negligence of the stevedores. Thus the reasonable person should foresee that his or her act would cause the plaintiff some harm. The defendant would thus be liable for all direct consequences of his act even though they were not foreseen.

Directness v remoteness The consequences of a defendant's act can be endless and the law cannot take into account everything that follows from a wrongful act. A plaintiff who has established loss caused by the defendant's wrong may therefore be unable to recover damages because the loss is too remote from the wrongful act, in other words the damage is not sufficiently connected with the defendant's act.

OVERSEAS TANKSHIP(UK) LTD V MORTS DOCKS & ENGINEERING CO LTD

In *Overseas Tankship(UK) Ltd v Morts Docks & Engineering Co Ltd* [1961] AC 388, the defendants discharged oil from their ship into Sydney Harbour and left port six hours later. The oil, carried by wind and tide, came beneath the plaintiff's wharf some 200 yards away from where welding operations were in progress. A piece of molten metal fell from the wharf and ignited a piece of floating rag on the oil. In a resulting fire the wharf was severely damaged. The defendant neither knew nor ought to have known that the oil was capable of being set alight when spread on water and the resultant damage was held to be too remote from the original act. Two principles emerge from this case:

- a defendant is only liable for the damage which a reasonable person would have foreseen as a likely consequence of an act;
- a defendant is only liable to compensate for damage that was foreseeable and not all the direct consequences of the act.

Where the consequences of an act are direct because one consequence flows automatically from another and cannot be avoided then the *Re Polemis* rules will apply. However, if there is an interruption, diversion or an intervening and new physical event, the chain of causation is broken and the result will be held to be too remote.

Employers have a common duty of care

WILSON'S & CLYDE COAL CO V ENGLISH

The leading case to illustrate this duty is *Wilson's and Clyde Coal Co v English* [1938] AC 57. The employer tried to argue that he had discharged his duty by employing a mine manager whose responsibilities included safety. A miner was leaving the pit when the haulage system was put into operation. He was crushed against a wall before he had time to reach a refuge hole. It was held that it was an unsafe practice for the haulage system to be operated while the morning shift was leaving work.

The House of Lords held that it was the personal duty of the employer to take reasonable care for the safety of their workforce and that this duty was threefold:

- to provide safe plant and machinery;
- to ensure he employs competent staff;
- to provide safe systems of work.

This is a personal duty because the employer is the person in control of the work and any dangers. They cannot relinquish their responsibility for undertaking any of the three duties mentioned above and must take reasonable care in all circumstances.

The duty to provide competent staff

An employer should not employ or continue to employ a person at a particular task for which he or she is not qualified or insufficiently experienced where to do so would possibly endanger his or her fellow employees. The employer can be held liable for the negligence of their staff. This is known as vicarious liability and is examined below.

HUDSON V RIDGE MANUFACTURING CO LTD

In *Hudson v Ridge Manufacturing Co Ltd* [1957] 2 QB 348 (see above), Hudson broke his wrist because of the action of a fellow employee who was known for playing practical jokes. It was held that it was the employer's duty to reprimand, discipline or dismiss a fellow employee of Hudson in order to remove this danger.

The duty to provide adequate material, premises and plant

Where an employee is injured because of some defect in the materials, equipment or plant in circumstances where the employer did not take reasonable care to make them safe, the employee can pursue an action for negligence. If the employer showed that they had taken reasonable care in buying equipment from a reputable supplier this was held to be an adequate defence.

However, where common law appears to be unfair, statute law is often introduced to rectify this. For example, the Employers' Liability (Defective Equipment) Act 1969 stipulates that the employee can make a direct claim against the employer, who can in turn sue the supplier or manufacturer of the equipment. An employer now has to provide tools of the right quality, and sufficient tools and equipment for the job.

The duty to provide a proper system and effective supervision

A system of work is a practice which is permanent and continuous, and not merely a method which is casual and emerging in a day's work. It can cover the physical layout of a job, the sequence in which the work is undertaken, the provisions of warnings and notices, and the issue of special instructions.

RUSHTON V TURNER BROS ASBESTOS CO LTD

In *Rushton v Turner Bros Asbestos Co Ltd* [1959] 3 AER 517, it was stated that 'an experienced workman must know the ordinary risks of the work which he is employed to do. In doing that work he is expected to take the ordinary routine precautions which are common to it, and should not expect to be told by his employer of every danger which might arise and every step that should be taken to counteract that danger.' Thus, an employer's duty is to initiate and maintain a safe system of working where there is a real risk of injury, some degree of complexity or unfamiliarity in the work, and where some practicable precaution can be taken.

Vicarious liability

Vicarious liability is defined as being where one person is held to be liable for the behaviour of other persons acting on his or her behalf. It would be unfair to make an employer a target for a common law claim as a result of all negligent behaviour of people acting on their behalf, so a set of rules has been established by which to judge the extent of this liability. An employer may be liable both for the torts of their employees and those of independent contractors (a tort is a civil wrong).

Liability for the torts of employees exists where:

- a wrongful act or omission has been expressly authorised by the employer, or the employer has implied that it should be authorised;
- a wrongful act or omission is committed by doing something authorised by the employer in an unauthorised manner;
- a wrongful act or omission is committed and ratified by the employer.

Before liability can be proved it has to be shown that:

- the employee is a true employee (is paid and is subject to normal procedures of hiring and dismissal);
- the employee has committed a tort or crime;
- the tort was committed in the course and scope of the employee's employment, for example doing what he or she was employed to do.

There are several defences available to an employer which either rebut the allegation of negligence, or attribute the damage or accident to a circumstance which is beyond their control. They can plead that as they took reasonable care there was no negligence, or that no duty of care was owed in the first place. There are also some specific defences as follows.

The first is *novus actus interveniens* (a new act has intervened). This covers the actions of a third party between the negligent act and the subsequent damage to the injured person. It is the function of the court to decide if the intervening act could have been reasonably foreseen by the defendant.

SCOTT V SHEPHERD

In *Scott v Shepherd* [1773] 2 WmBL 892, the defendant threw a lighted squib on to a market stall whose owner quickly threw it to another stall. The next stall owner did the same, eventually injuring the plaintiff. The defendant was held to be liable because the chain of causation had not been broken by a new act.

The second is *volenti non fit injuria* (no harm can be done to a willing person). This defence is used to show that the injured person was aware of the risk involved in the action and consents to it.

BOWATER V ROWLEY REGIS CORPORATION

In the case of *Bowater v Rowley Regis Corporation* [1944] KB 476, the plaintiff, an employee of the defendant, was asked to take out an unruly horse and cart. He protested at this, but the foreman insisted that he should do as he was told. The horse bolted and Bowater was injured. The defendants were held to be negligent. The defence of *volenti non fit injuria* failed because it was held that 'a man cannot be said to be truly willing unless he is in a position to choose freely. Free choice requires (a) knowledge of the danger, and (b) the absence in his mind of any feeling of constraint.' Thus, compliance with an employer's request is not normally taken to be consent.

HAYNES V HARWOOD

A second type of case where this defence will fail is where a person has been under a moral or legal duty to act. In the case of *Haynes v Harwood* [1935] 1 KB 146, a policeman was injured when he tried to control Harwood's horse which had bolted in a crowded street. Haynes seized the horse to stop it injuring innocent bystanders. The court held that the defence of *volenti* failed because the police officer assumed the risk involved in tackling a horse and cart which was out of control through his legal duty.

CUTLER V UNITED DAIRIES

In a parallel case, *Cutler v United Dairies* [1933] 2 KB 297, Cutler assisted a dairyman in catching a runaway horse. In the course of this Cutler was injured. United Dairies were successful in their defence of *volenti non fit injuria* because Cutler was not intervening to rescue people from injury and he had time to consider the risk, and was deemed to have implicitly consented to this.

Contributory negligence

Contributory negligence describes the behaviour of an injured person whose actions contributed to the occurrence giving rise to his or her injuries. Until the Law Reform (Contributory Negligence) Act 1945 this was held to be a complete defence. Now damages are reduced for the plaintiff in proportion to the amount that their own negligence contributed to their injury.

SAWYERS V HARLOW UDC

In *Sawyers v Harlow UDC* [1958] 2 All ER 342, the plaintiff entered a public lavatory owned by Harlow UDC. Owing to a defective lock that jammed, she could not get out and while attempting to climb out, she fell and injured herself. It was held that the defendants were negligent, but that the award should be reduced by 25 per cent because she tried to balance on a revolving toilet-roll holder.

OLIVER V BIRMINGHAM BUS CO

In *Oliver v Birmingham Bus Co* [1932] 1 KB 35, it was held that a young child cannot be guilty of contributory negligence even if accompanied by an adult. A four-year-old in the company of his grandfather was run over by a bus when the grandfather let go of his hand while crossing the road. The damages were not reduced.

JONES V BOYCE

The 'agony of the moment' is a defence to contributory negligence, as illustrated in *Jones v Boyce* [1816] 1 Starkie 493, where a coach passenger believed the coach he was riding in was about to crash due to the driver's's negligence and jumped off, breaking a leg. The coach did not crash. It was held that there was no contributory negligence and he could recover from the defendant as he had acted reasonably in the 'agony of the moment'. Contributory negligence cannot be applied where the principle of alternative danger exists. If the negligence of the defendant puts the plaintiff in a position of imminent personal danger, the plaintiff's conduct, even if it results in personal harm, does not amount to contributory negligence if his or her conduct is reasonable in the 'agony of the moment'.

Implications of the common law for the management of an effective safety campaign

An employer's duty consists of the provision of safe plant and materials, competent staff and safe systems.

WOODS V DURABLE SUITES

In *Woods v Durable Suites* [1953] 1 WLR 857, a common problem was ruled on. This concerned the misuse or non-use of personal protective equipment. The employer was a furniture manufacturer. Woods was

---

an experienced glue spreader. Durable Suites knew that there was a real risk of dermatitis in Woods's work and to counteract this risk they provided barrier cream and washing facilities. They also ran an extensive poster campaign about the danger of contracting dermatitis and the use and importance of using precautions. They also told Mr Woods personally about the risk which, as an experienced man, he already fully understood. The level of supervision was such that the employers did not know that Mr Woods was not taking the proper precautions and as a result he contracted dermatitis. It was ruled that the defendants had discharged their responsibilities by running an appropriate safety campaign. Further, it was also held that the amount of energy expended had been appropriate to the risk to which employees were exposed.

Therefore, a personnel manager responsible for safety must ensure that:

- the employee is aware of any dangers associated with the job;
- the employee knows what precautions must be taken in view of those dangers;
- the precautions that are necessary are always available for use; and
- the employee knows that the precautions are available for use.

To achieve these aims an energetic safety campaign has to be undertaken to get the message over to employees. You will not have discharged your common law duty of care simply by issuing safety equipment or protective clothing if you do not educate your employees as to why these are necessary. You should be able to demonstrate that you have undertaken group and/or individual training exercises. Further, you must demonstrate that you ensure, so far as it is reasonably practicable, that employees take these precautions. Supervision must ensure that precautions made available by the employer are used, otherwise the employer may be held liable in the event of an accident.

Common law duties to non-employees

In essence, the degree of responsibility will be proportional to the amount of control the occupier has over the visitor. Sometimes the occupier may have so much control over the activities of the visitor or user that their duty is as high as if the relationship were that of employer and employee. This is particularly the case where the visitor is a contractor's workman working under the instruction of the occupier. The civil liability of an occupier of land or buildings or fixed or movable structures such as vehicles and scaffolding towards persons coming lawfully on to those premises is laid down in the Occupier's Liability Act 1957.

The extent of an organisation's responsibility will depend on the type of work being carried out. If one employment is more dangerous than another, a greater degree of care must be taken by the employer. If employers are not able to eliminate the risk, they must at least take reasonable care to reduce it as far as possible. Employers must take reasonable care to ensure the safety of their employees' workplace even when it involves work at another occupier's premises. However, in the latter case, the employer can only be expected to take limited precautions. The employer must ensure, however, that proper safety equipment and instruction is given.

Under section 2 of the Occupier's Liability Act 1957, the occupier must take reasonable care to see that their visitors are reasonably safe in using the premises for the agreed purposes of the visit. The same duty is owed to all lawful visitors, including people with a legal right of entry such as HSE inspectors, utility engineers etc. The Act makes provision for the circumstances of the visitor, for example, children will be less careful than adults.

GLASGOW CORPORATION V TAYLOR

In the case of *Glasgow Corporation v Taylor* [1922] 1 AC 44, a seven-year-old child died after eating some poisonous berries from a shrub in a public park which was under the control of the Corporation. The Corporation were found liable as they knew the berries were poisonous and that children used the park, but did nothing to give effective warning of the danger to children.

MOLONEY V LAMBETH LBC

In *Moloney v Lambeth LBC* (1966) 64 LGR 440, the local authority was held liable to a four-year-old who fell through a gap in a balustrade in a block of corporation flats. Under the Occupier's Liability Act 1984, the organisation has a statutory duty of care to trespassers and other uninvited persons. This duty can normally be discharged by giving warnings and discouraging people from incurring the risk. There is no duty to persons who willingly accept the risks once they are aware of and understand them. Warning signs must be clear, unambiguous and use standard pictorial representations as specified under British Standards Institute BS5378 Part 1.

The organisation has a twofold duty of care with regard to contractors, namely both a responsibility to them and for them. Liability rests with the person in control (the occupier). Control, however, may be divided between different occupiers.

Division of control

WHEAT V LACON

In the case of *Wheat v Lacon* [1966] AC 552, control was divided between the brewery in charge of the public house and the manager who lived in part of it. In this particular case, a visitor to a public house was fatally injured. Both owner, brewery, occupier and licensee would have been liable under the Occupiers Liability Act, 1957, had it not been for a technicality of the law. The court took the view that since the owners could control the use to which a licensee puts the premises they were to some extent in control. The division of blame in such a case will depend on how the accident occurred and whose particular responsibility it was to avoid it. It is possible for visiting contractors or subcontractors to become occupiers of the whole or part of the premises if they are the only people involved in working there. This can be achieved by handing over control of the worksite to the contractor within a physical boundary for a specified time period.

However, there are two circumstances which are likely to put liability back on to your organisation. The first is where your own employees have recourse to the area occupied by the contractor (you are still, in effect, occupying that part of the premises and have a personal duty to your employees). The second circumstance is where your organisation has been negligent in its choice of contractor and has selected someone who is not competent to do the job safely.

A PERSONNEL MANAGERS CHECKLIST

- Have they done this kind of work before?
- How much experience do they have?
- Can anyone furnish references as to the quality of their workmanship?
- What provisions will they make for the safety of your employees?
- What guarantees do they give for completion and performance of contract?
- Have you specified safe working practices?
- Have you checked compliance on a regular basis so far as it is reasonably practicable?

If the dangers are caused by contractors working on the occupiers' premises, the Occupier's Liability Act 1984 states that the occupier is not liable if he or she has taken reasonable care to see that the premises are safe.

There are however, four circumstances where the manager and the organisation cannot escape liability.

1. Where the employer asks the contractor to break the law.

ELLIS V SHEFFIELD GAS CONSUMERS CO

In *Ellis v Sheffield Gas Consumers Co* [1853] 2 E&B 767, the company employed a contractor to dig up streets in Sheffield even though they had no legal right to authorise this. The contractor's workmen left a pile of stones in the street over which the plaintiff fell and was injured. The defendants were held liable for the consequences of their unlawful act.

2. Where the operation is on or adjoining a public highway other than for the normal use of the highway.

TARRY V ASHTON

In the case of *Tarry v Ashton* [1876] 1 QBD 314, Ashton (the occupier) hired a contractor to repair a heavy lamp attached to the front of his house and overhanging the street. The repair was carried out negligently and the lamp collapsed injuring Tarry. It was held that the occupier was liable in that he failed to discharge his duty by not ensuring that the lamp was maintained. That this was due to the negligence of a third party was no defence.

3. Where the contractor is employed to undertake extrahazardous activities.

HONEYWILL & STEIN V LARKIN BROS

In the case of *Honeywill & Stein v Larkin Bros* [1934] 1 KB 191, the plaintiffs instructed Larkin to photograph the interior of a cinema and in the process the cinema was set on fire due to a magnesium flash being used. The cinema owner successfully claimed damages from Honeywill & Stein, who in turn sought indemnity from Larkin Bros.

Any person who brings onto his lands anything likely to do mischief and it escapes, must keep it at his peril, or be answerable for the consequences should it escape.

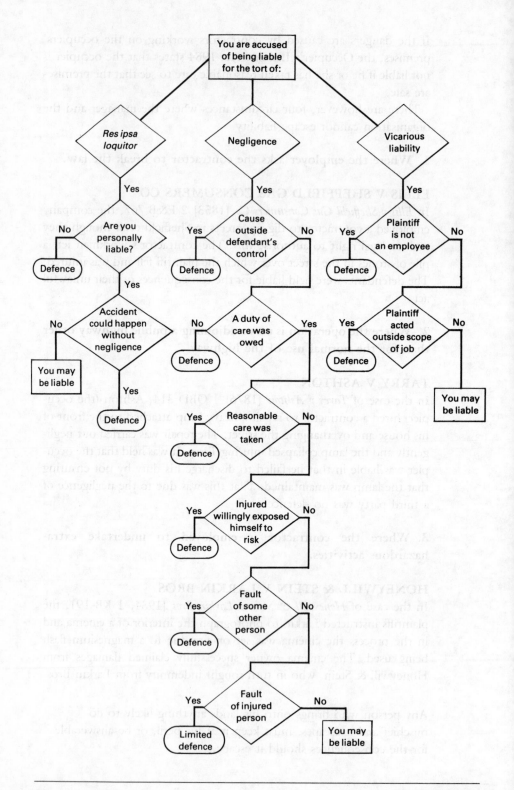

TAKING CARE OF SAFETY

RYLANDS V FLETCHER

In *Rylands v Fletcher* [1868] LR 3 HL 330, this precedent was established when contractors constructing a reservoir on Fletcher's land negligently plugged a disused mineshaft which connected with Rylands's mine. When the reservoir was filled with water, it escaped through the mineshaft, flooding Rylands's mine.

4. Where the occupier knows or ought to know of risks to visiting contractors which are not occupational hazards, but which are peculiar to premises.

WOOLLINS V BRITISH CELANESE

In *Woollins v British Celanese* (1966) 110 SJ 686, the occupier was held to blame for an unusually fragile roof which was held not to be a normal hazard for a post office engineer who injured himself when he fell through the roof.

Criminal liability

Acts of Parliament impose duties upon all of us. For example, we must insure our vehicles if we drive one on the public highway, we must sell goods fit for the purpose, we must not allow certain rooms to fall below a certain temperature, etc. These duties are enforceable by punishments which are usually decided by a court unless a fixed penalty has already been agreed and established. Statute law governs matters that affect the State as a community. In safety management terms, certain statutes allow for a person injured as a result of a breach of the law to bring civil proceedings against the other for the injuries received. However, most, if not all statutes, place general standards of conduct upon people and these are usually not very specific. It is then up to judges to interpret the law in order to test whether such action was meant and covered by the statutory act.

This may also mean that an employee injured because of a breach of statutory duty may also claim as a result of negligence. It is equally as feasible to win on one point and lose on the other as it is to lose or win both. It must be said that an employee winning on both points does not necessarily get double damages.

It is useful for the personnel manager to compare the statutory responsibilities towards employees with the duties imposed by the common law.

Figure 1.2 Some examples of defences

Failure to comply with a statutory duty is a crime and prosecutions can be initiated in a variety of courts.

- **Magistrates' court** The proceedings are relatively inexpensive and quick. The vast majority of criminal cases in England and Wales are dealt with here. Typically, three magistrates will try summary offences specified by statutes, for example, most of the offences listed in section 30 of the Health and Safety at Work Act 1974 (HASAWA) are summary offences and carry a punishment of a fine up to £2,000 (see below).

   The HASAWA makes provision for some offences that are triable either summarily or on indictment. Magistrates can offer the defendant the choice of trial for a hybrid offence either in the magistrates' court or, after preliminary consideration, by a Crown Court.

- **Crown Court** Proceedings are more expensive and usually slower. The Crown Court deals with indictable offences. The court can impose a sentence of an unlimited fine and/or a maximum of two years' imprisonment.

- **Court of Appeal** Very expensive but proceedings can be relatively quick. It can dismiss or allow an appeal, order that a conviction recorded in a lower court be quashed and, finally, order a retrial.

- **House of Lords** Proceedings are extremely expensive and relatively slow. Law Lords only become involved with cases which involve an important point of law of general precedent or interest.

Statutory duties of employers

An important statutory duty is placed on the occupier of a factory under the **Factories Act 1961**. Generally, the issues contained in the Act cover the areas of health, safety and welfare.

In the area of health, such things as cleanliness, ventilation, toilet facilities, lighting, working temperatures, drainage and overcrowding are covered. Safety issues include machinery fencing, hoists, chains, obstructions, fire escapes etc, while welfare covers first-aid facilities, washing and rest facilities, provision of drinking water etc. These points are quite specific and action for damages can be brought for loss suffered through a breach of these duties and responsibilities.

The Factories Act 1961 applies to all factories of whatever size, irrespective of the number of employees and the type of trade or business being carried out. The definition of a factory is very long and appears to be based upon the employment of manual labour. For example, a canteen within the physical bounds of the factory used for feeding and entertaining the workers is deemed to be part of the factory, yet a restaurant used solely by management is not. This is based upon the distinction that feeding and entertaining the workers is not incidental to the normal processes of the factory, but to feed the management is. So, presumably, a person injured while cleaning the workers' canteen could get damages, but a person injured while cleaning the managers' restaurant would not!

While factories are covered by the Factories Act 1961, the Offices, Shops and Railway Premises Act 1963 covers the occupiers of offices, shops and railway premises. The Act deals with the same issues covered by the Factories Act and includes advice on health, safety and welfare issues. Workers in agriculture and forestry are similarly provided for in the Agriculture (Safety, Health and Welfare Provisions) Act 1956, while the Mines and Quarries Act 1954 provides rules for the control and management of mines and safety including roof supports, ventilation, protection against dust, winding apparatus, construction and fencing of machinery and the use of explosives. An action for breach of statutory duty of these three Acts lies on the same principles as those which apply to the Factories Act.

It was not until the introduction of the HASAWA in 1974 that full protection was provided to all at work (except those in private domestic employment), including workers on oil rigs and other offshore installations. Earlier laws were unaffected by this piece of legislation and the HASAWA enables regulations and codes of practice to be altered with relative ease. This is a particularly important feature since technology in some industries is known to move faster than the law. An example of this occurred following the Flixborough Nypro Chemical explosion in 1974, after which the Health and Safety Commission established an advisory committee on major hazards and it published new guidelines in 1976.

The main thrust of the HASAWA comes in section 2 where an employer's duties to his or her employees are discussed. Briefly these are:

- the provision and maintenance of plant and systems of work that are, so far as is reasonably practicable, safe and without risk to health;
- arrangements for ensuring, so far as is reasonably practicable, safety and absence of risks to health in connection with the use, handling, storage and transport of articles and substances;
- the provision of such information, instruction, training and

supervision as is necessary to ensure, so far as is reasonably practicable, the health and safety at work of employees;

- so far as is reasonably practicable as regards any place of work under the employer's control, the maintenance of it in a condition that is safe and without risks to health, and the provision and maintenance of means of access to and egress from it that are safe and without such risks; and
- the provision and maintenance of a working environment for employees that is, so far as is reasonably practicable,

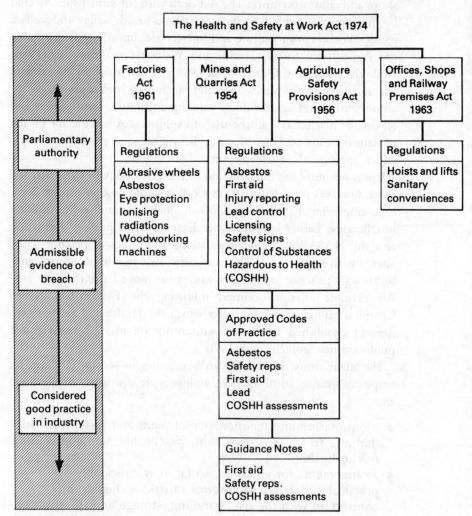

Figure 1.3 The Health and Safety at Work Act 1974 and its relationship to other statutes and regulations

safe, without risks to health and adequate as regards facilities and arrangements for their welfare at work.

Safety practitioners find the legislation of immense value, but are frustrated as to the vagueness of the repeated statement 'where reasonably practicable'. What might be deemed by one person to be reasonably practicable, may not be deemed so by another. The best way to clarify the confusion is to examine how judges have interpreted this matter in court.

'Reasonably practicable' is a narrower term than 'physically possible' and seems to me to imply that a computation must be made by the [employer] in which the quantum of risk is placed on one scale and the sacrifice involved in the measures necessary for averting the risk (whether in money, time or trouble) is placed on the other; and that, if it is shown that there is gross disproportion between them – the risk being insignificant in relation to the sacrifice – the defendants discharge the onus on them.

Unlike the common law which places the burden of proof on the plaintiff, the HASAWA places the onus of proving the limits of what was reasonably practicable with the accused. It is important to show the court under these circumstances that this assessment was made before the charges were laid, for example before the alleged offence had taken place. And remember that lack of money or resources is no defence.

Section 2 of the HASAWA then goes on to outline the general areas to be considered by the employer when complying with the general duties already described.

General duties of employers

Employers should ensure the following:

1. (a) fire precautions taken
   (b) sufficient lighting
   (c) sufficient working space
   (d) clear unobstructed gangways
   (e) tidy workplace, floors in good condition
   (f) steps, stairs, ladders, scaffolding etc in good condition
2. (a) dangerous machinery to be guarded
   (b) regular inspection and maintenance procedures
   (c) emergency stop buttons
   (d) sufficient equipment of the right quality

3. (a) correct procedures laid down
   (b) safety equipment
   (c) clear instructions
   (d) permits to work in extra-hazardous areas
4. (a) adequate ventilation
   (b) reasonable temperature
   (c) accidents promptly investigated
   (d) first aid facilities
   (e) washing facilities
   (f) sanitary conveniences
   (g) cleanliness of workplace
   (h) waste disposal etc
5. (a) instructions, training etc
   (b) protective clothing and equipment for mechanical handling equipment
   (c) forklift trucks, conveyors, trolleys etc
   (d) storage areas defined.

Factors to be considered when discharging your duty towards contractors' employees include:

- the competence or specialist skills possessed by the contractors and their workforce;
- the amount of control you have over their activities;
- whether or not you are providing plant and equipment for their use;
- what dangers exist in the workplace that the contractor ought to be warned of;
- any areas which may contain potential hazards of which you are not aware.

Five general duties are concerned with physical aspects of work and environment:

- safe place of work with a safe means of access and exit;
- safe plant and equipment – including maintenance;
- safe systems of work;
- safe working environment, and adequate facilities and arrangements for employees' welfare;
- safe methods for handling storing and transporting goods.

Then there are duties concerning the physical aspects of the work environment and of the people who are employed:

- provision of information, instruction, training and supervision;

- trade unions must be allowed to appoint safety representatives from within their membership and management have no say in these appointments;
- employers of more than five people must prepare and revise, where appropriate, a written statement of policy in respect of health and safety (safety policy).

The provision of information, instruction, training and supervision ties in very closely with your common law duty to provide competent staff, not only so that the interests of fellow employees are guarded, but also so that the individual employee is better equipped to take care for their own safety. You should not overlook the training of supervisors when considering this aspect.

It is important to recognise the extent of the employer's duties in relation to those of the employee. It would seem that the employee will only be liable if he or she does something outside the control of his or her employer and/or unknown to him or her, or in direct contravention of instructions given by his or her employer.

The amount of reasonable care or co-operation expected of the employee will depend heavily on the amount of instruction, training and information he or she has been given. The amount of supervision necessary will equally depend upon these three things and as the amount of information, instruction and training given to the employee increases, the amount of supervision will decrease. This does not mean to say that supervision is no longer required, but that it may be reduced to take account of the growing skill and experience of the individual employee.

Statutory duties to non-employees

So far we have only discussed the duties of employers to their employees, but employers also have a duty under statute to people who are non-employees. There are two aspects of this duty.

1. **Employers and self-employed** Responsibilities involve the actual operation of the business and working practices.
2. **Occupiers of premises** Responsibilities involve the premises and ownership of plant and materials.

The relationship between the employer (as a client) and independent contractors has been the subject of much debate. Where the organisation's employees are called to work jointly with the employees of contractors, one of the questions which might arise is that of responsibility for the provision of information, instruction and training for the two groups of employees. To some extent the judgment in the following case has answered this question.

REGINA V SWAN HUNTER SHIPBUILDERS LTD

In *Regina v Swan Hunter Shipbuilders Ltd* [1979] ICR 831, in 1976, an accidental fire occurred on board *HMS Glasgow*, under construction at the Swan Hunter yard, which caused the deaths of eight Swan Hunter men and injured three others who were working on it.

A leak of oxygen from a hose left below deck at the end of shift, occurred in the period 22–23 September, causing oxygen enrichment (about 40%) of the atmosphere on one of the lower decks. A fierce fire occurred on the morning of 23 September when a welder struck an arc.

Instructions to Swan Hunter employees had included a requirement to bring oxygen and fuel gas hoses to the top deck at the end of the shift, though there were no notices posted to this effect and it was known that the practice was not consistently observed.

In relation to non-employees, ie contractors and subcontractors involved in the welding operations, Swan Hunter did nothing to ensure that they were aware of the hazards of oxygen enrichment and the precautions to be taken. Furthermore, they did not satisfy themselves that safe practice was observed and had no procedure for monitoring the practices adopted by contractors.

The Committee of Inquiry recommended that Swan Hunter introduce a system to monitor precautions in the use of oxygen and fuel gases by both employees and contractors, that they should ensure that all concerned were aware of the hazards and that sufficient instruction was given to enable danger to be avoided.

As a result of the accident Swan Hunter were prosecuted under sections 2 and 3 of the HASAWA on the basis that if the provision of a safe system of work for the benefit of employees involves information and instruction of the potential dangers being given to persons other than employees, then the employer is under a duty to provide such information and instruction.

It is, therefore, important for employers to ensure that the provision of information about dangers peculiar to their places of work or processes extends to persons other than their own employees who may be affected by them, or whose actions may affect the health and safety of their own employees.

In addition it would be advisable to provide instruction on the safe use of equipment available on the premises or on the proper precautions to be observed to minimise the risk of accidents occurring. It may also be necessary to give verbal or written instruction, to provide safety manuals or information leaflets and, in special circumstances, to provide training to persons other than direct employees.

These responsibilities would typically include the following areas:

- ensure that staff are trained and competent to carry out their tasks;
- ensure that sufficient information and instruction is given;
- ensure that plant, machinery and equipment in the department is safe and properly maintained;
- ensure safe access and egress within the department;
- ensure a safe place of work;
- ensure that fire precautions are taken.

Hybrid offences

All other offences specified by the HASAWA are triable either way, for example:

- failure to discharge a duty imposed by sections 2–7;
- contravention of sections 8 and 9;
- contravention of any health and safety regulation;
- contravention of an improvement or prohibition notice;
- illegal disclosure of certain kinds of information;
- making a false statement or entry to a register or document, or forging a document with intent to deceive;
- impersonating a factory inspector.

Certain offences actually carry the full sanction of a prison sentence and these are as follows:

- a breach of the requirements of a prohibition notice;
- a breach of the conditions of issue of a licence;
- attempting to acquire explosives;
- the disclosure of information given under certain circumstances by the Health and Safety Commission.

The first ever prison sentence as a result of a prosecution under the HASAWA was given in 1985 to a company director who 'demonstrated a cynical disregard for the dangers to health'. The individual was also personally fined a total of £1,500, along with fines to his company totalling £2,000. The director failed to comply with a prohibition notice served on the removal of asbestos lagging. His one-month prison sentence was suspended for two years.

Trade unions see health and safety training as purely their province and representatives are entitled by law to attend a TUC approved course, this principle having been tested in an industrial tribunal. However, this should not be the beginning and end of their training.

Union courses should be supplemented by in-house training dealing with issues specific to the organisation's work. Ideally the courses should produce a balance between instruction, training and information as discussed above.

Other forms of guidance

Other forms of guidance and advisory literature will generally fall into one of the following categories.

- **Guidance notes by the Commission** These will be authoritative in so far as they carry the Commission's backing, but they will fall short of approval of any particular course of conduct by an employer.
- **Guidance notes by the Health and Safety Executive (HSE)** These will essentially be working notes of guidance. They will for example include advice on requirements to be followed and action to be taken by employers in order to comply with the law, technical data about specific hazards, and the interpretation of biological data by medical officers.
- **Guidance notes by industry advisory committees** These will originate in the form of reports which will carry the authority of the individual committee.
- **Guidance notes issued by industry** Industry-generated notes of guidance may come from manufacturers and other associations providing technical and common-sense instructions on how to cope with various situations in particular workplaces. The Commission or the HSE will normally not wish to give any official recognition to these guidance notes.

Failure to comply with statutory requirements may lead to prosecution for breach of a statutory duty. Most safety cases are heard in the magistrates' court summarily, but the more serious ones are heard on indictment in the Crown Court. Do not forget that unlike under common law, there does not have to be an injury before action can be taken by the HSE inspector (see below).

Health and Safety at Work Act 1974

The HASAWA is likely to impinge most directly on those managers who are held primarily responsible for compliance with the Act in their company. The Act determines specific standards of safety in a number of areas through regulations issued under its provisions. The Act imposes a number of legal duties on employers, the self-employed, employees, suppliers and owners of premises, to ensure that their workplaces are safe and offer no risk to health. The Act has four basic aims:

- to secure the health, safety and welfare of persons at work;
- to protect persons, other than persons at work, against risks to health and safety arising out of or in connection with the activities of persons at work;
- to control the keeping and use of dangerous substances;
- to control the emission into the atmosphere of noxious and offensive substances.

To achieve these aims the Act has established one comprehensive, integrated system of law dealing with health and safety and the welfare of people at work, and the public who may be affected by such work activities. In so doing it:

- places general duties on the employer, ranging from providing and maintaining a safe place of work to consulting with employees;
- places duties on employees to take reasonable care of themselves and anyone who may be affected by their work activities, and to co-operate with their employer and others in meeting these obligations.

The Act is a piece of enabling legislation which allows the Secretary of State to define a system of regulations and approved codes of practice which will progressively replace the existing legislation, but will maintain or improve the standard of health, safety and welfare established by the Act. Thus, the regulations can be amended to keep pace with developments.

Implications of the Act

1. ACCOUNTABILITY

It can be seen that sections 2, 3 and 4 of the Act impose wide-ranging and far-reaching duties on the organisation by virtue of its position as employer and controller of premises. However, the Act does not stop with the inanimate 'body corporate'. Section 7 makes it the employee's duty to have a care for him or herself and for others who may be affected by his or her acts or omissions at work, also placing on him or her a duty to co-operate with the employer to enable the requirements of sections 2, 3 and 4 to be complied with. Sections 33, 36 and 37 make it an offence for an individual to fail to discharge the duties placed on him or her by sections 2–7 and remove the 'protection' afforded by the body corporate. Not only can the organisation be prosecuted for offences under the Act, so can the managing director and his subordinates right down the management chain, where it can be established in law that they have failed to comply. Therefore, wherever a person holds a management position, the responsibility conferred with that post includes responsibility under the Act commensurate with the status of their post. Further to this, section 8 refers to 'persons' who shall not interfere with or misuse anything provided in the interests of health, safety and welfare. Thus, any person who misuses or vandalises a first-aid box or fools about with a fire extinguisher can be prosecuted under this section of the Act.

2. CONTROL OF PREMISES

Section 4 of the Act is applicable where persons who are not employees of the organisation, including members of the general public, are on the premises of the organisation. The plant or substances affected range from an ordinary chair to an arc welder, or from water to a radioactive isotope.

3. SAFETY INFORMATION AND TRAINING

Section 2(2)(c) requires the employer to provide information, instruction, training and supervision. Much of this requirement devolves on the manager as follows.

- **Information** This will be passed down from the relevant department. Where applicable and relevant, information must be brought to the notice of affected employees by the responsible manager. Additionally, information applicable to the safety of a particular process or piece of equipment must be readily available for employees to study.
- **Instruction and training** The basis of much of health and safety awareness is effective instruction and training. While much of this will originate from and be organised by the responsible department, the manager has to ensure that all members of his or her staff receive the relevant and required instruction and training. Additionally, because of sections 3 and 4 of the Act, in certain circumstances 'persons not employees' may also need to be trained.
- **Supervision** The appropriate level of supervision must be exercised at all times. It is not sufficient to provide information, instruction and training without adequate supervision in safety matters. Such supervision must primarily be directed at ensuring that all subordinate staff have regard to safety issues. Managers must consider the adequacy of the level of supervision in possible

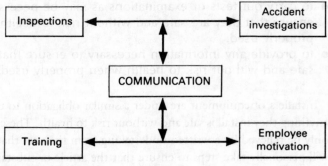

Figure 1.4 Performance appraisal

hazardous areas, particularly in the light of the experience of the employees involved.

4. DUTY NOT TO CHARGE

Section 9 places a duty on the employer not to charge the employee in respect of anything done or provided in pursuance of any specific requirement of the relevant statutory provisions. Thus, where there is a statutory regulation requiring certain things to be done, such as the Protection of Eyes Regulations which requires operators to have eye protection, this must be provided free of charge. Where practicable all protective clothing should also be provided free of charge.

5. DUTY OF MANUFACTURERS

Section 6 places a duty on the manufacturer and the supplier broadly to make and supply articles and substances which are, as far as is reasonably practicable, safe and without risk to health for use at work. Employers and individual managers must ensure that instructions provided by a manufacturer or supplier are brought to the attention of and obeyed by employees.

6. SUPPLIERS' DUTIES

Section 6 the HASAWA places responsibilities upon the suppliers of equipment and materials. In fact, section 6 covers the responsibilities not only of suppliers, but also of designers, manufacturers and importers, and installers of articles and substances intended for use at work.

These are:

● to ensure that these articles and substances are safe and without risk to health when properly used.

- to carry out tests or examinations as may be necessary to ensure that they are safe and without risk to health when properly used.
- to provide any information necessary to ensure that they are safe and without risk to health when properly used.

Installers of equipment are under a similar obligation to ensure that anything they install is safe and without risk to health. These duties can only be relieved by a written undertaking from the user that he or she will personally take steps to ensure that the article or substance will be made safe.

It you may be felt that the duties of your suppliers have no relevance to you or your organisation or that they may even relieve you of your responsibility as a user of equipment. There are, however, two important factors which you must consider.

First, as a user of equipment you have a responsibility to your employees to provide (so far as is reasonably practicable) equipment and materials that are safe and without risk to health. You cannot rely upon the integrity of the supplier in every instance to protect the safety of your staff. It is necessary for you, the user, to request information from the supplier in order to enable you to use the article or substance safely. Furthermore, if an article or a substance has a defect or is a risk to health and safety and it can be shown that you were (or should have been) aware of this, it is no defence to argue that it was supplied in that condition. You may find that you share liability with the supplier.

Secondly, your organisation may itself be a supplier of articles or substances for use at work and consequently may incur the liabilities imposed by section 6. This often happens where items surplus to requirements are disposed of by selling them on to others who may intend to use them at work.

Safety representatives and committees

A unionised employer has a duty to consult with safety representatives appointed by the appropriate trade union. Where two or more safety representatives request that a safety committee be formed, an employer must undertake the establishment of such a committee under section 2(7) of the HASAWA and the Safety Representatives and Safety Committees Regulations 1977, reg 9(1), within three months of the request being made (see, further, Chapter 3, *Safety Representatives and Committees*).

Enforcement of the health and safety provisions

The safety laws within an organisation's premises are enforced by the HSE. Primarily, this agency seeks to advise and assist employers in meeting the appropriate standards, although they do have broad powers of enforcement.

The HSE inspectors have a number of powers available to them and when appointed they are issued a warrant card which specifies the range of these. They include the power:

- to enter premises at any reasonable time;
- to take a police constable if necessary.
- to take any authorised person and equipment, for example, gas or electricity engineers;
- to examine or investigate accidents or dangerous occurrences;
- to require premises or the scene of an accident to be left undisturbed;
- to take samples of suspect substances etc (they must leave an equivalent sample for independent analysis should you wish it);
- to dismantle or test any dangerous article or substance;
- to take possession of any dangerous article or substance for examination or for use in legal proceedings;
- to require information facilities and assistance to carry on these duties;
- to require the production of any relevant books or documents;
- to seize, destroy or render harmless any article or substance which is a source of imminent danger;
- to interview employees, take statements and require a written declaration of the truth of these statements.

The following offences carry a maximum £2,000 fine on summary conviction:

- preventing or hindering a person appearing before an inspector;
- intentionally obstructing an inspector.

Enforcement notices

The HASAWA brought about an innovation in the enforcement of safety legislation by giving inspectors the power to issue improvement or prohibition notices. Each serves a specific purpose as follows.

IMPROVEMENT NOTICE

An inspector may serve an improvement notice where he or she is of the opinion that a contravention of a statutory requirement has been or is about to be carried out. This requires the person on whom the notice is served to make the necessary improvements to reach the desired standard. The inspector may specify appropriate remedial action and give a time limit of not less than 21 days in which to comply.

The minimum time period is important because it is the time allowed for the person to appeal to an industrial tribunal against the terms of the notice. An appeal may take two forms:

- appeal on the grounds that the notice and remedial action is not reasonable;
- that the time allowed is not sufficient in which to comply.

When an appeal is lodged it has the effect of suspending the notice until the appeal is heard and decided.

It is important to note that an improvement notice cannot be served where the breach has already taken place and is not likely to be repeated. Under these circumstances the inspector may choose to prosecute.

PROHIBITION NOTICE

A prohibition notice can be served where an inspector is of the opinion that an activity being carried on or about to be carried on may give rise to serious personal injury. There does not have to be a breach of a statutory requirement. The notice takes effect immediately but, unlike the improvement notice, an appeal (within 21 days) does not have the effect of suspending the notice.

Failure to comply with either notice is an indictable offence and may result in prosecution with severe penalties. For example, on conviction, a person will be liable to an unlimited fine and/or imprisonment for a term not exceeding two years.

The lesson here is not to ignore a notice once it has been served just because you disagree with it. This is an offence in itself, even if the notice *is* unreasonable! The best approach under these circumstances is to lodge an appeal and argue the issue of reasonableness in front of a tribunal.

Prosecution

An inspector may choose a third course of action and that is to prosecute the person responsible for committing the offence. This person may be the employer, the employee, individual managers and directors, or any other person assigned responsibilities by the HASAWA.

SUMMARY OFFENCES

An inspector may prosecute for the following breaches:

- contravening a requirement imposed by an inspector under section 20 or 25 of the HASAWA;
- preventing a person from answering an inspector's question;
- obstructing an inspector while carrying out his/her duties;
- contravening a requirement imposed by a committee of inquiry or obstructing a person acting under its direction.

Aspects of personal liability

The general duty of employees is covered by section 7 of the HASAWA which says that each employee shall take reasonable care for his or her own health and safety, and that of other people. The main factors to be considered when deciding whether reasonable care has been taken are the magnitude of the risk involved in the activity and the cost of the precautions necessary for averting the risk.

Other factors to be considered are the obvious nature of the risk and also whether or not the risk is inherent in the job, for example steeplejacks, miners, etc.

Employees are also required to co-operate with employers to enable them to carry out their statutory duties. This applies to all employees regardless of status, whether they are operators, managers or directors.

However, if your job involves instructing other people in what they must do then the HASAWA places an extra duty on you to avoid causing these people to commit an offence. Section 36 says:

Where a person by his act or default causes another person to commit an offence then he, as well as that other person, may be charged with the offence.

Hence, if you instruct one of your staff to do something which is in contravention of one of the statutory requirements you may be found guilty of the offence. Several managers have fallen foul of this section.

The issues relating to senior managers and directors are more complex. It is recognised that employers are merely organisations of people and that offences committed by the organisation may have been due to the acts of one or more of its senior managers. Section 37 says:

Where an offence committed by a body corporate is shown to have

---

been committed due to the consent connivance or neglect of a director or senior manager then he as well as the body corporate shall be guilty of the offence.

Someone then, must make or neglect to make the decisions that affect the safety and well-being of the organisation and its employees, and that individual must be accountable in law.

In a case arising from a serious accident in which the injured party lost four fingers when they became trapped in the rolls of a copying machine, section 37 of the HASAWA was used to prosecute the senior office manager. He was given the responsibility of checking the safety of the machine guards under his company's safety policy.

The HASAWA has therefore provided a vehicle for the prosecution and punishment of individuals who break the safety laws and put themselves and others at risk.

An important consideration, along with the responsibilities placed on them by the HASAWA, is the extent and domain of responsibility given to individual managers and directors by the organisation's safety policy. The purpose of assigning these responsibilities is to maintain standards of safety in the workplace by giving individual specific tasks relating to the safe performance of their activities. In fact, where these responsibilities are clearly defined by the policy, the individual may incur criminal liability for failing to discharge them.

For example, a director was prosecuted following a fatal accident to one of his employees on the evidence that he had failed to perform a duty of which he knew or ought to have known. He had, in fact, failed to comply with a company circular requiring him to devise a safety policy for his department and to inform and train his employees in the requirements of the HASAWA.

More recently, the first ever prison sentence was imposed upon a director of a company who ignored a prohibition notice issued by an HSE inspector. The court said, 'You have demonstrated a cynical disregard for the dangers to health. I am satisfied your motive was profit.' The prison sentence of one month was suspended for two years.

Safety then, is the employer's responsibility, but it is clearly seen as also being the responsibility of the management in any organisation or business.

Managerial responsibility

Typical managerial duties set down in a safety policy may include any or all of the following:

- to ensure that you and your staff understand and implement the organisation's health and safety policy;
- to ensure that you and your staff are aware of their legal and common law duties relating to health and safety at work;
- to ensure that any special regulations which apply to operations carried out under your control are made known and observed, and to see that all procedures are properly carried out;
- to see that job safety requirements are listed and made known to operatives by satisfactory safety training;
- to assist your staff in resolving health and safety problems and seek assistance as appropriate from the organisation's safety officer;
- to ensure that you and members of your staff attend regular meetings at which health and safety can be discussed;
- to make sure that the reporting of all accidents and dangerous occurrences is done in order to enable investigations to be carried out and to accept the advice given to prevent recurrence;
- to ensure that there is provided adequate levels of supervision, suitably qualified and knowledgeable staff on safe working procedures and practices;
- to ensure that all employees within your control are provided with such information, instruction and training to enable them to work safely within organisation and statutory safety requirements, both at the induction stage of employment and during all employment activities;
- to ensure that all required safety equipment is made available for use by those employees who need to use them;
- to conduct periodic safety inspections or contribute to safety inspections of the area for which you are responsible and to implement improvements as required. This management involvement is crucial to the success of the safety policy.

When judging your safety record you probably looked at the number of accidents your company had over a specified period of time, and compared this with the organisation's accident rate. If you used this measure you might relax in the knowledge that your department has relatively few accidents. However, while this may be comforting news, a more important question to be answered is, 'How much is this good accident record related to the amount of activity you have undertaken in promoting and maintaining safety standards?' for more on this, see Chapter 8.

Employee motivation

- How many employees were contacted personally about safety matters?
- How many positive reinforcements of behaviour were given?
- How many negative reinforcements of behaviour were given (reprimands or corrections)?
- What media have been utilised for this purpose, for example, films, posters, letters etc?

Your personal contact with employees is important in generating an awareness of health and safety. The more interest you show the more likely employees are to co-operate with you in promoting health and safety.

Safety is the responsibility of management and should be managed the same as any other activity within the organisation. However, while management normally accept the responsibility of dealing with matters such as production, industrial relations and the utilisation of plant and equipment etc, they are generally not so careful about ensuring compliance with the safety rules. This is often because the internal penalties for failure in this area are not so clearly defined – managers rarely get sacked for a poor safety record. This should not, however, encourage you to relax your activities in this area.

Selection of contractors

All the effort you put into providing for the safety of your staff may be undone by the activities of contractors in your workplace. It is important to:

- take reasonable care to select competent contractors;
- supervise the activities of contractors where their work brings them into contact with your employees.

The common law places an obligation on occupiers of premises to take reasonable care in the selection of contractors. If part of your job includes the hiring of contractors to carry out certain activities, this responsibility falls on you. You may be helped in this by your organisation's policy on the employment of contractors. Many specific organisations now carry lists of approved contractors who can be relied upon to work to an acceptable standard. These contractors must be used whenever possible.

In the absence of clear guidelines you should ensure that, in the right circumstances, they have a safety policy outlining the arrangements and procedures of their companies for safe working.

Where the contractor is required by law to have a safety policy, you should ask for it to be presented with the tender for the contract. If the contractor has less than five employees they are not required to have a written safety policy and therefore should be required simply to give assurances about safety when they are carrying out the work.

These contractors should be required to work in accordance with your organisation's safety policy and given information, instruction and training where necessary to enable them to carry out their duties safely. Where there is uncertainty you may find it helpful to consult your organisation's safety adviser.

1. Supervision and monitoring Where the work is carried out in an area under your control you are responsible for ensuring that your staff and members of the public are not put at risk. You will be faced from time to time with decisions relating to the work of contractors.

2. Permission to start work All contractors should report to the manager of the affected area before work commences. (There will also be a requirement for them to report to the clerk of works or engineering department for longer contracts).

3. Use of organisation's equipment Contractors are expected to provide their own tools, plant and equipment necessary for the satisfactory performance of the work in hand. Use of the organisation's equipment should be by written permission of the organisation's representative. Contractors should also ensure that their employees are provided with any necessary personal safety equipment, for example helmets, goggles etc.

4. Fire extinguishers Contractors should familiarise themselves with the location of fire extinguishers in the area in which they are working. If additional extinguishers are required these should not be obtained from other locations, but from the engineering department.

5. Fire alarm systems Contractors should make themselves aware of the positions of the fire alarm call point and the organisation's fire procedure.

6. Interference with fire equipment Except for use in an emergency, any interference with the electrical wiring and other mechanism of automatic fire detection and extinguishing apparatus, or of the audible fire warning system, should be prohibited. Requests for temporary resetting of such equipment must be made to the engineering department.

7. No smoking areas The no smoking rules in all areas where smoking is forbidden should be strictly observed. Consideration must also be given to the use of welding equipment, blow lamps etc, and also to the safe storage and use of flammable materials.

8. Warning of danger Care must be taken at all times to protect the organisation's employees, property and work in progress from danger, and any circumstances which give rise to such danger must be reported immediately.

9. Accidents All accidents, injuries and dangerous occurrences should be reported to the manager.

10. Unused materials Contractors should be required to remove all unused materials and leave the site clean and tidy on completion of the work.

11. Housekeeping Contracts should ensure that the workplace is kept tidy with no dirt or refuse being allowed to accumulate.

These points are relevant guidelines to be applied to contractors where their work interfaces with the activities of your employees. Other, more technical, aspects that need to be considered which take into account the needs of both employees and members of the public include the following.

- **Electricity, gas, air mains** On no account should use be made of the organisation's electricity, gas or compressed air mains, without the permission of the organisation. Where permission is granted the method of connection should be approved by the engineering department.
- **Excavations** Before any excavation work is begun, the architects or technical services should be consulted about the existence of electric cables, drains, air, gas, and water mains.
- **Fencing excavations** Excavation or projecting equipment should not be left at any time without taking the necessary safety precautions. All excavations, and openings, should be securely fenced and these and any obstructions marked by a sufficient number of lamps during hours of darkness. During the excavation of all such work, the surrounding area should be maintained in a state of tidiness. Loose materials of whatever kind should not be left about or allowed to obstruct roadways, gangways or working areas.
- **Building operations** All building work should be carried out

strictly in accordance with the regulations made under the Factories Act, in particular complying with the requirements for scaffolding and access equipment.

These provisions, though not exhaustive, could form the basis of a supervision checklist which you would use to assess the activities of contractors.

Remember, just because they are not your employees does not mean to say that you have no responsibility for them. Many of these duties are interrelated, but in principle it is the responsibility of the party in control of, or carrying out, the activity to foresee any possible harm and take reasonable steps to prevent it. This is complicated by the fact that some areas of responsibility may be shared by two or more parties so that clear procedures need to be laid down to avoid confusion. This is particularly so where contractors are working alongside your own employees and members of the public.

Above all there is a need to ensure that all parties are aware of the risks involved by providing information, instruction and training, and by ensuring that their activities are supervised and monitored.

By considering all these points you will not only help to ensure the safety of employees and others, but also help to avoid incurring liability on both you and your employer.

Within the enforcement area of safety management is that of policing. To ensure that organisations are conducting their business within the terms of the HASAWA, the HSE was set up. At the same time, the Health and Safety Commission was created to oversee the work of the HSE. The Commission has the general power of overseeing the work of the Executive and has power to delegate to it. However, the Executive is a statutory body charged with the responsibility for the enforcement of safety legislation. The Commission cannot give instructions or directions to the Executive about enforcement matters and cannot issue judgements in any particular case. Both Commission and Executive are rather bureaucratic and cumbersome.

Some relevant acts of parliament

Legislation has consolidated the common law rules of employers' liability and has given rise to a civil liability to pay compensation.

Employers' Liability (Defective Equipment) Act 1969

This Act made the employer liable for the fault of the manufacture of defective equipment. The employer will have to pay the employee compensation. They will then be able to claim their money back from the manufacturer. This is known as the principle of loss distribution.

Employers' Liability (Compulsory Insurance) Act 1969

This Act makes it obligatory for most employers (except nationalised industries, local authorities and the police) to insure against liability for injury to employees. Failure to buy such insurance or display a certificate of insurance can lead to fines on a daily basis of up to £500 and £200, respectively, under the Criminal Law Act 1977.

Occupiers' Liability Act 1959

This imposes duties on occupiers of premises. Where an employee goes to work on third party premises, his or her employer is liable if the employee is injured through the employer having failed to set up a safe system of work. However, if the employee is injured by a structural defect in the premises which is not incidental to the work, the employer is not liable. The injured person must sue the occupier of the premises. This will only succeed if there are unusual dangers which the occupier knew or should have known about. Until the Unfair Contract Terms Act 1977, it was possible for the occupier to contract out of their liability by posting a warning notice and condition.

Congenital Disabilities (Civil Liability) Act 1976

This Act makes it possible for a child, who is born disabled as a result of a breach of common law or statutory duty to a parent, to sue the parent's employer.

Fatal Accidents Act 1976

This allows dependents of employees killed at work through the employer's negligence, to sue the employer for damages. Compensation is assessed on the actual or prospective earnings of the deceased breadwinner.

Law Reform (Miscellaneous Provisions) Act 1934

This allows the person entitled to the property of a deceased employee killed at work, to inherit any right of action against the employer which the deceased person might have had.

Limitations Act 1975

This controls the time period within which actions must be brought against the employer. The period is normally three years from the date when the cause of the action began. The cause of action begins when the injured employee had the necessary legal and medical knowledge to realise that he or she had a probable right to sue his or her employer.

Some other relevant legislation is given in Table 1.1 in the form of a checklist. While this list might not be exhaustive, the personnel manager should enlarge upon it and attempt to keep it up to date. A blank checklist is provided for this purpose in Table 1.2.

Regulations

Regulations proposed by the Commission, accepted by the Secretary of State and duly laid down before Parliament, become the law of the land and are duly enforceable through the courts. Breaches of duties imposed by health and safety regulations (where they cause damage) are actionable in civil proceedings unless they specify otherwise. For example, the HASAWA specifically excludes sections 2–9 from being actionable at common law for breach of a statutory duty. New regulations may place an absolute duty on employers in the same way as some existing provisions do, or they may be limited by the use of phrases such as 'so far as practicable' and 'so far as reasonably practicable'. 'Reasonably practicable', on the other hand, enables account to be taken of differing circumstances.

Where the word 'practicable' is used it is generally taken to mean that which is possible in the light of current knowledge and invention. For example, it is impossible to take precautions against a danger which is not known to exist, or to take precautions which have not yet been invented.

Approved codes of practice

The Commission's power to approve and issue codes of practice is contained in section 16 of the HASAWA. The objective of these codes is to provide practical guidance on the requirements contained in sections 2–7 of the Act, or in health and safety regulations, or in any of the existing statutory provisions. The precise statutory requirement to which the approved code is supplementary must be indicated in the code itself.

The purpose of the code of practice is to:

● specify in greater detail or in a more liberal style than is practicable or desirable in regulations, the precise technical and other requirements to be observed in a particular set of regulations or other relevant statutory provisions;

Table 1.1 *A personnel manager's checklist*

Legislation	Does it apply to you?		Have you a copy		Do you understand it?	
	YES	NO	YES	NO	YES	NO
Health and Morals Act 1833						
Factory Act 1833						
Mines and Collieries Act 1842						
Workshop Regulations Act 1967						
Metalliferous Mines Regulation Act 1872						
Explosives Act 1875						
Factory and Workshop Act 1878						
Employers' Liability Act 1880						
Shop Hours Regulation Act 1886						
Factory and Workshop Act 1901						
Alkali Works Regulation Act 1906						
Coal Mines Act 1911						
Anthrax Prevention Act 1919						
Employment of Women, Young Persons and Children Act 1920						
Celluloid and Cinematograph Film Act 1922						
Explosives Act 1923						
Petroleum Consolidation Act 1928						
Children and Young Persons Act 1933						
Hours of Employment (Conventions) Act 1936						
Petroleum (Transfer of Licences) Act 1936						
Public Health Act 1936						
Children and Young Persons (Scotland) Act 1937						
Factories Act 1937						
Hydrogen Cyanide (Fumigation) Act 1937						
Public Health (Drainage of Trade Premises) Act 1937						
Young Persons (Employment) Act 1938						
Law Reform (Contributory Negligence) Act 1945						
Ministry of Fuel and Power Act 1945						
Coal Industry Nationalisation Act 1946						
Radioactive Substances Act 1948						
Factories Act 1948						
Law Reform (Personal Injuries Act) 1948						
Shops Act 1950						
Rag Flock and Other Filling Materials Act 1951						
Rivers (Prevention of Pollution) Act 1951						
Fireworks Act 1951						
Agriculture (Poisonous Substances) Act 1952						
Emergency Laws (Miscellaneous Provisions) Act 1953						
Mines and Quarries Act 1954						
Agriculture (Safety, Health and Welfare Provisions) Act 1956						
Clean Air Act 1956						
Occupiers' Liability Act 1957						
Factories Act 1959						
Radioactive Substances Act 1960						
Factories Act 1961						
Offices, Shops and Railway Premises Act 1963						
Nuclear Installations Act 1965						
Civil Evidence Act 1968						

Legislation	Does it apply to you?		Have you a copy		Do you understand it?	
	YES	NO	YES	NO	YES	NO
Trade Descriptions Act 1968						
Employers' Liability Act (Compulsory Insurance) Act 1969						
Employers' Liability Act (Defective Equipment) Act 1969						
Public Health (Recurring Nuisances) Act 1969						
Equal Pay Act 1970						
Fire Precautions Act 1971						
Industrial Relations Act 1971						
Mines Management Act 1971						
Employment Medical Advisory Service Act 1972						
Control of Pollution Act 1974						
Health and Safety at Work Act 1974						
Trade Union and Labour Relations Act 1974						
Water Resources Act 1974						
Limitations Act 1975						
Sex Discrimination Act 1975						
Social Security Act 1975						
Social Security (Consequential Provisions) Act 1975						
Fatal Accidents Act 1976						
Food and Drugs (Control of Premises) Act 1976						
Race Relations Act 1976						
Road Traffic Regulation Act 1976						
Trade Union and Labour Relations (Amendment) Act 1976						
Criminal Law Act 1977						
Unfair Contract Terms Act 1977						
Employment Protection (Consolidation) Act 1978						
Refuse Disposal (Amenity) Act 1978						
Employment Act 1980						
Limitation Act 1980						
Magistrates Court Act 1980						
Local Government, Planning and Land Act 1980						
Administration of Justice Act 1982						
Derelict Land Act 1982						
Social Security and Housing Benefits Act 1982						
Supply of Goods and Services Act 1982						
Criminal Justice Act 1982						
Food Act 1984						
Road Traffic Regulation Act 1984						
National Health Service (Amendment) Act 1986						
Safety at Sea Act 1986						
Sex Discrimination Act 1986						
Fire Safety and Safety of Places of Sport Act 1987						
Consumer Protection Act 1987						
Road Traffic Act 1988						
Local Government Act 1988						
Road Traffic (Driver Licencing and Information Systems) Act 1989						
Companies Act 1989						
Environmental Protection Act 1990						

Table 1.2   *A personnel manager's checklist*

Legislation	Does it apply to you?		Have you a copy		Do you understand it?	
	YES	NO	YES	NO	YES	NO

TAKING CARE OF SAFETY

- explain what in particular circumstances would be considered to constitute satisfactory compliance with the requirements of a general obligation.

It was the intention of Parliament that an approved code of practice should enjoy a new and special status and would in effect provide a simple and flexible extension of the law. This special status is given by section 17 which states that failure to observe any provision of an approved code shall not of itself render a person liable to criminal or civil proceedings, but where in criminal proceedings a person is alleged to have contravened a statutory requirement or prohibition, the court is required to admit in evidence any provisions of an approved code which appear to it to be relevant. Further, where the court considers that provisions of the code are relevant, then failure to observe those provisions is to be taken as proof of a contravention, unless the court can be satisfied that you have complied with the requirement in another way.

Approved codes will usually be generated by the Commission, the HSE, industry advisory committees set up by the Commission, or possibly in conjunction with such a body as the British Standards Institution. Codes generated elsewhere will not normally be approved by the Commission unless they are felt to be a necessary and suitable extension of the law.

Assessing what is reasonably practicable

ASSOCIATED DAIRIES V HARTLEY

An illustration of the term 'reasonably practicable' is to be seen in the case of *Associated Dairies v Hartley* [1979] 1 RLR 175. A worker was injured when a wheel of a lorry ran over his toe. The employer had provided safety shoes which could be purchased at cost by the workforce. The cost was spread over a period of time. An inspector issued an improvement notice requiring Associated Dairies to issue the shoes free of cost. The employer appealed. The tribunal thought that it would be practicable for the employer to provide the shoes without cost, but that it was not reasonable to expect them to do so. The time, trouble and expense of safety precautions must be weighed against the foreseeable risk and in this case, the expenditure by the employers would be disproportionate to the risk.

Offences under the Act and those other safety and health laws mentioned above are deemed criminal and may involve prosecution of an individual or a company in a magistrates' or Crown Court. It is a fundamental principle of criminal law for the prosecutor to prove beyond reasonable doubt that the offence was committed by the accused. Under section 40 of the HASAWA, it is for the accused to prove that they took reasonably practicable precautions as required by the Act, and by some sections of the other health and safety laws. This means that if the accused thought that it was not reasonably practicable to take certain steps then it is for him or her to provide the proof.

A checklist of some of the relevant regulations in force is given in Table 1.3. Personnel managers should attempt to keep this up to date on a blank checklist given in Table 1.4.

The Council of the European Communities

Since the formation of the EC, it must not be forgotten that the European Parliament may issue directives which will influence policies and strategies within Member States. For example, the Commission to the Council of the European Communities under Article 118A of the Treaty provides that the Council shall adopt, by means of Directives, minimum requirements for encouraging improvements regarding the health and safety of workers, especially in the working environment. Article 15 of this Directive states that Member States shall bring into force the laws, regulations and administrative procedures necessary to comply with this Directive by January 1, 1991. The Directive covers the following areas:

- objectives;
- definitions;
- responsibilities of employers;
- obligations of the employer;
- preventative services;
- information to be collected and held by employers;
- information and communication with workers;
- consultation with the workforce;
- training;
- obligations placed on workers;
- adoption of individual directives concerning the workplace, equipment, personal protective equipment, work and visual display units and the handling of heavy loads involving the risk of back injury.

While the law places statutory obligations upon organisations such as those described above it is important that these are implemented efficiently and effectively. In subsequent chapters we shall discuss how this can be achieved.

Summary

It is not possible here to provide an in-depth study into the health and safety legislation of the UK. It is intended rather to remind those already familiar with the law and to provide an introduction to the lay person or student. A reading list is provided for those wishing to learn more about this complex area. Personnel managers only need as good a working knowledge of the law as would any professional manager. Expert advice should be sought as and when appropriate owing to the complexities of the law in this regard. Despite the wealth of safety case law in existence at the present time, it is always a communication problem in getting the 'lessons learnt' aspects of the cases across to safety practitioners. Many safety practitioners experience great difficulty in this area. It is essential, therefore, that safety managers have direct access to legal expertise. At the present time, there is a bewildering mass of legislation which lays both criminal and civil responsibilities upon employers. Among aspects covered are the style and manner of accident reporting, and the safe access to buildings and sites, and particular regulations governing dangerous materials or processes such as asbestos and steam boilers. Special constraints are placed on the employment of children and young persons. Construction and building operations, because of their high-risk nature, are highly regulated. Procedures for the control of industrial major accident hazards, and the use and transportation of dangerous substances have all been introduced in the 1980s.

Exceptional care has to be taken in handling the relationship between safety and discipline, and unfair dismissal even though employees' duties are tightly defined. Distinct regulations apply to electrical and fire hazards within the Factories Act. Specific provision has to be made for appropriate first-aid facilities. It must be stated that with regard to enforcement, draconian consequences both for civil and criminal liability may be felt by board members down to low-level supervisors. Specific controls relating to food handling and hygiene, use of lifting machinery and materials' handling are all covered. Chronic problems which may be felt by employees in terms of noise and vibration, overcrowding or problems of occupational health have all been strengthened in the last three years. Liability may also exist for product and structural safety, as well as personal protection. Certain categories of workers, including women and those who work at heights or off shore, are afforded additional protection under the law.

In the UK as in Europe, regulations, Directives or decrees are introduced from time to time to deal with issues which have been found to

Table 1.3 *Some statutory instruments, rules and orders*

Some statutory instruments, rules and orders	Does it apply to you?		Have you a copy		Do you understand it?	
	YES	NO	YES	NO	YES	NO
Factories, Locomotives and Sidings Regulations 1906						
Factories (Horsehair Processes) Regulations 1907						
Factories (Electrical Energy) Regulations 1908						
Factories (Tin or Terne Plates Manufacturing) Order 1917						
Tanning (Two-Bath Process) Welfare Order 1918						
Fruit Preserving (Welfare) Order 1919						
Laundry Workers (Welfare) Order 1920						
Celluloid (Manufacturing) Regulations 1921						
Chemical Works Regulations 1922						
Electric Accumulator Regulations 1925						
Herring Curing (Scotland) Welfare Order 1926						
Bakehouses Welfare Order 1927						
Manufacture of Cinematograph Film Regulations 1928						
Oil Cake Welfare Order 1929						
Cement Works Welfare Order 1930						
Sugar Factories Welfare Order 1931						
Sanitary Accommodation Regulations 1938						
Cinematograph Film Stripping Regulations 1939						
Electricity (Factories Act) Special Regulations 1944						
Patent Fuel Manufacture (Health and Welfare) Regulations 1946						
Clay Works (Welfare) Regulations 1948						
Dry Cleaning Special Regulations 1949						
Pottery (Health and Welfare) Special Regulations 1950						
Factories (Testing of Aircraft Engines) Regulations 1952						
Iron & Steel Foundries Regulations 1953						
Petroleum Spirit (Conveyance by Road) Regulations 1957						
Agriculture (Avoidance Of Accidents to Children) Regulations 1958						
Agriculture (Safeguarding of Workplaces) Regulations 1959						
Agriculture (Threshers and Balers) Regulations 1960						
Construction (General Provisions) Regulations 1961						
Agriculture (Field Machinery) Regulations 1962						
Washing Facilities Regulations 1964						
Examination of Steam Boilers Regulations 1964						
Power Presses Regulations 1965						
Construction (Working Places) Regulations 1966						
Construction (Health and Welfare) Regulations 1966						
Carcinogenic Substances Regulations 1967						
Offices, Shops and Railway Premises (Hoists and Lifts) Regulations 1968						
Asbestos Regulations 1969						
Abrasive Wheels Regulations 1970						
Foundaries (Protective Footware and Gaiters) Regulations 1971						
Highly Flammable Liquids and Petroleum Gases Regulations 1972						
Organic Peroxides (Conveyance by Road) Regulations 1973						
Agriculture (Tractor Cabs) Regulations 1974						
Industrial Tribunals (Improvement and Prohibitions) Regulations 1974						
Woodworking Machines Regulations 1974						
Protection of Eyes Regulations 1974						
Employers' Health and Safety Policy Statements (Ex) Regulations 1975						

Table 1.3 *Continued*

	Does it apply to you?		Have you a copy		Do you understand it?	
Some statutory instruments, rules and orders	YES	NO	YES	NO	YES	NO
Protection of Eyes (Amendment) Regulations 1976						
Safety Representatives and Safety Committees Regulations 1977						
Health and Safety (Enforcing Authority) Regulations 1977						
Motor Vehicles (Construction and Use) Regulations 1978						
Control of Lead at Work Regulations 1980						
Safety Signs Regulations 1980						
Dangerous Substances (Conveyance by Road) Regulations 1981						
Diving Operations at Work Regulations 1981						
Health and Safety (Dangerous Pathogens) Regulations 1981						
Health and Safety (First-Aid) Regulations 1981						
Notification of Installations Handling Hazardous Substances Regulations 1982						
Notification of New Substances Regulations 1982						
Asbestos (Licensing) Regulations 1983						
Control of Industrial Major Accidents Hazards Regulations 1984						
Criminal Penalties (Increase) Order 1984						
Classification, Packaging and Labelling of Dangerous Substances Regulations 1984						
Poisonous Substances in Agriculture Regulations 1984						
Social Security (Industrial Injuries) (Prescribed Diseases) Regulations 1985						
Reporting of Injuries, Diseases and Dangerous Occurrences Regulations 1985						
Ionising Radiation Regulations 1985						
Industrial Tribunals (Rules of Procedure) Regulations 1985						
Building Regulations 1985						
Electrically Operated Lifts (EEC Requirements) Regulations 1986						
Dangerous Substances in Harbour Areas Regulations 1987						
Control of Asbestos at Work Regulations 1987						
Control of Substances Hazardous to Health Regulations 1988						
Pneumoconiosis (Workers Compensation) (Specified Diseases) Regulations 1988						
Ionising Radiations (Protection of Persons Undergoing Medical Examination or Treatment) Regulations 1988						
Classification, Packaging and Labelling of Dangerous Substances (Amendment) Regulations 1989						
Pressure Systems and Transportable Gas Containers Regulations 1989						
Public Service Vehicles (Temporary Driving Entitlement) Regulations 1989						
Road Traffic (Carriage of Explosives) Regulations 1989						
Road Vehicles Lighting Regulations 1989						
Freight Containers (Safety Convention) Regulations 1989						
Road Traffic Accidents (Payment for Treatment) Regulations 1990						
Social Security (Industrial Injuries and Diseases) Misc Provisions 1990						
Collision Regulations (Seaplanes) (Amendment Order) 1990						
Dangerous Substances (Notification and Marking of Sites) Regulations 1990						
Smoke Control Areas (Authorised Fuels) Regulations 1990						
Personal Injuries (Civilians) Regulations, 1990						
Cosmetic Products (Safety) (Amendment) Regulations 1990						
Fire Safety and Safety of Places of Sport Act 1987 (Commencement Order No 6) Order 1990						

Table 1.4 *A personnel manager's statutory instruments, rules and orders update checklist*

Some statutory instruments, rules and orders (updates)	Does it apply to you?		Have you a copy		Do you understand it?	
	YES	NO	YES	NO	YES	NO

be dangerous or hazardous to health. These regulations might cover such subjects as the use of circular saws or washing facilities. They are usually introduced following evidence to the enforcement agencies that such guidance is necessary. This is an established practice in the Western world and covers all aspects of safety. For example, evidence was provided that alcohol was a contributory factor in road accidents. Most developed countries have legislated, or issued decrees or regulations, which clearly point out the consequences of drinking alcohol and driving, following evidence gained from accident analysis. In the same way industrial enforcement agencies gather similar evidence which assist in introducing appropriate measures designed to reduce or prevent such occurrences happening in the future. Senior management must appreciate that the rules are made to help, not hinder, the organisational mission. On the other hand, regulating against some malpractice does not necessarily prevent it from happening. People still injure themselves on chain saws, still drink and drive and still suffer ill health carrying on some activity contrary to good advice or legal necessity.

Finally, the law must be regularly monitored. It is important to establish as early as possible the implication of each set piece of legislation so that appropriate management decisions can be taken. Keeping abreast of current legislation and/or regulations can be time-consuming and it is important to know where to seek advice quickly and easily. This will require the establishment of systems and practices designed specifically to inform organisations of their legal obligations at regular intervals. This could include attendance at training courses, seminars and conferences which may be either external or in-house. The implication of new regulations upon an organisation are important. The question most likely to be asked of a safety manager is in relation to the cost to the organisation. This will require a detailed reply. The procedure for doing this must form part of the daily management plan. These issues are discussed in subsequent chapters dealing with safety management planning and implementation.

With industrial accidents increasing each year it is clear that the law alone is unable to control this epidemic effectively. For effective accident reduction strategies we require a co-ordinated strategy which some refer to as the safety mix or 4E strategy. This refers to *environmental* strategies, such as making the workplace safer or healthier; *engineering* by making machinery and tools safer; *education* programmes designed to raise the awareness of all problems in the workplace; and *enforcement* which covers the relevant law. The management of safety must be seen as a corporate issue which demands the skills of properly trained safety managers (or personnel officers where an organisation is unable to employ a qualified safety practitioner) who are capable of using all the resources within an organisation. They must have a sound understanding of latest developments within the 4E philosophy and have sufficient authority within the organisation to implement sound proactive policies.

CHAPTER 2
The Role of the Personnel Officer

The role of the personnel manager needs to be defined, and this is the purpose of this chapter. We shall be looking at gathering information and analysing data, planning remedial strategies and implementing a programme, following this with a look at programme monitoring and evaluation. The safety mix is also dealt with plus some notes on monitoring health and safety policy.

Introduction to the role of personnel officer

Any personnel manager charged with the responsibility of carrying out an organisation's health and safety policy must do so efficiently and effectively. To do this, it is important that the manager concerned is aware of his or her duties, responsibilities and functions. To assist in this you should remember that there are seven basic tasks to consider.

First, you will have to act as an accident investigator. Second, you will need to plan policies, procedures and programmes designed to reduce accidents or prevent them from happening. Accident prevention also means the inclusion of all health matters. Third, you will need to monitor regularly all health and safety policies, procedures, practices and programmes to ensure satisfaction. Fourth, you will be required to provide on-the-job instruction and training in safe systems of working, workplace rules and regulations, employee responsibilities, and indoctrination and education. Fifth, you will be required to provide and issue protective clothing and/or equipment in accordance with the law and appropriate regulations. You will also be required to maintain a safe environment in which you expect people to work. If you are in any doubt whatsoever about your duties and responsibilities you should know when and how to seek help. Sixth, you should get to know and understand your workforce. Do not expect an employee to do a job you know nothing about. You should be seen to lead by example. If hats are required to be worn on the shop floor then that rule applies to *all* employees including the personnel staff. Finally, you have a duty to ensure that health and safety matters are given a high priority within the decision-making process. It is important to secure recognition of the importance of health and safety at senior level, and sufficient resources should be allocated to the tasks.

These tasks are summarised in Table 2.1 below.

The major areas of responsibility for the personnel manager concern the formulation, implementation and monitoring of appropriate action. Personnel managers have to manage other staff and as such are faced with their planning, organisation, motivation and control. Since the introduction of the Health and Safety at Work Act (HASAWA) in 1974, organisations have had a statutory obligation to ensure the safety

Table 2.1 *General tasks for the personnel manager*

Task	Specific activity
Accident investigator	To carry out investigations into all accidents and dangerous occurrences in order to establish contributory factors.
Advocate	Establish health and safety as a priority within the organisation and secure its recognition at board level. Secure sufficient resources.
Auditor	Carry out regular examinations of current health and safety policy, procedures, practice and programmes to ensure satisfaction.
Leader	Know and understand the workforce and lead by example. Motivate workers and develop schemes and plans to change attitudes and behaviour.
Planner	Plan, implement, monitor and evaluate remedial measures designed to reduce or prevent accidents from happening.
Provider	Issue protective clothing and/or equipment. A knowledge of the legal requirements is necessary. Seek expert help where necessary.
Trainer	Provide on-the-job training, safe systems of working, indoctrination, workplace rules and regulations, and employee responsibilities.

and well-being of their employees. This is a general piece of legislation covering broad safety principles, while other forms of legislation such as the Factories Act 1961 or the Fire Precautions Act 1971 are more specific (as we saw in Chapter 1). Some organisations react more enthusiastically than others in implementing such legislation. In this chapter, therefore, we will consider the implications of the HASAWA which place a broad statutory responsibility on employers to ensure the health, safety and welfare of their employees at work, and discuss the daily operational management plan required to deal with this responsibility.

Gathering information

In order to make decisions, certain information is required. There are a number of sources of information which are useful when planning, implementing, monitoring and evaluating health and safety policies, programmes and procedures. Information about what is happening in the workplace can be gleaned from:

- monitoring and evaluation;
- accident and dangerous occurrence investigation;
- personnel records;
- external sources.

Many companies monitor or evaluate their health and safety success via a number of commercially available *safety auditing* systems, while others opt for *in-house* methods. These systems are very useful for obtaining information with which to provide a safety rating or score. Very few firms base their strategies upon accident investigation and analysis techniques, and are therefore unable to show how effective they have been at reducing accidents or dangerous occurrences from year to year. The importance of a good accident investigation and analysis programme will be discussed further in Chapter 4.

When planning remedial action, the personnel manager will need to have access to various other types of information such as:

- the number of accidents resulting in injury which have occurred;
- the number of dangerous occurrences which have taken place;
- a detailed breakdown of each incident in sufficient detail to provide for the identification of cause and/or contributory factors;

- a sufficiently large database to allow for the identification of trends;
- supplementary information concerning accidents and dangerous occurrences from similar industries;
- relevant national statistics where they are available.

Although these issues will be dealt with in more detail in Chapter 4, it is important to realise at this point that this type of information is a vital part of the decision-making process and helps to provide for efficiency and effectiveness in practice.

Previous studies have revealed the poor quality of primary accident data collection procedures and the fact that maximum use of the information collected is not made. And even now, many of those charged with the responsibility for health and safety matters, continue to ignore or not to realise the value of a good, reliable primary data source. A strategic objective here, therefore, must include data collection and to ensure that these data are used for analysis purposes. This must form part of the decision-making process.

To do this within practical economic constraints, personnel managers should establish a system for collecting details of accidents and dangerous occurrences such as that outlined in Chapter 4. It is known that many organisations spend considerable sums of money in order to identify potentially dangerous situations. If an objective is to collect all accident information, then steps should be taken to collect this data in a sufficiently detailed form so that potential problem areas can be identified. This will enable priorities to be set and to ensure that resources are used effectively. At the same time, supplementary data should be systematically obtained from detailed, structured interviews with casualties so that lessons can be learnt. Wherever possible, these interviews should be in total confidence and without fear of any consequent disciplinary action.

We will now consider other forms of information that need to be collected. It has become established practice for the personnel manager to be primarily involved only in certain aspects of health and safety responsibility, such as education, training and publicity strategies, while the engineer or scientist concentrates upon engineering and some environmental issues. Such separation should be avoided wherever possible. To enable organisational missions to be met at all, and for efficiency and effectiveness to be improved, both systems should work closely together as each of them plan and implement strategies using the same database for decision making. Both are equally dependent upon the quality of these data and there should be a shared and co-ordinated approach to remedying any problems of unreliability. It is from this premise that other forms of relevant information can systematically be gathered for programme planning and evaluation purposes. Information gathering, therefore, is of great importance and should be given high priority within the objective-setting sequence.

Analysing data

The majority of managers responsible for health and safety do not have direct access to any database for decision-making purposes. In any case, few have received any relevant training on its use. An unacceptably high number of managers are unaware of its value and most have not considered whether their accident trends are a problem or not. Some managers collect accident data in order to establish trends but tend to analyse individual cases rather than establish causes. Furthermore, safety managers do not regularly monitor dangerous occurrences, nor are they familiar with the available statistical packages or research methodology. Few use even basic research tools such as computers. The problem can be compounded because some organisations pursue staff recruitment policies that are not designed to address this problem. In too many cases, companies fail to recruit numerate graduates for key management roles or to provide for adequate staff development in the areas of information technology and statistics. This is despite government departments, the Health and Safety Executive (HSE), Royal Society for the Prevention of Accidents (RoSPA) and the British Safety Council (BSC) regularly encouraging managers to evaluatee their work.

Planning remedial strategies

Planning remedial strategies can only effectively take place after all the relevant information has been thoroughly investigated and analysed. Central to the discharge of the safety manager's mission is the planning of appropriate remedial action, and education, training and publicity should be the main issues. A number of personnel managers still carry out the practice of preparing occasional visits around the company without defining the purpose or objective for such visits, or locating these visits within a broader pattern of provision. Others will write a 'memo' on a subject which may have been raised via the safety committee without first establishing whether the subject is a cause of concern by data analysis.

It is now accepted that for safety education to be effective it must be continuous and should, therefore, be part of the daily management plan. Clearly, the delegation of responsibility for this to all staff is necessary. Personnel managers are not appointed in large enough numbers to discharge such duties and responsibilities on their own. The role of the personnel safety manager should be seen, therefore, as that of adviser, supervising the development of remedial measures and their implementation, providing appropriate training and other materials, and trying to ensure that safety is given an appropriately high priority on the corporate agenda.

Programme implementation, monitoring and evaluation

The implementation of operational objectives needs careful consideration in two regards: first, the staff resource, and secondly, the financial resource. The accident database discussed earlier has to be the prime means of determining priorities. At the end of each year or time period when data is available, together with that for the previous two years, or period data, trends can be established and plans of action determined for the forthcoming year. The start of the new year or time period is an ideal time to be looking at objective setting in a company environment adopting a fiscal year or quarterly period; managers need to be aware of budget-making policies within their own organisation. It seems that a large number of personnel safety managers are not setting objectives or planning from any database, let alone considering operational objective setting as a process. Instead, programmes based upon precedent seem to be the norm, rather than planning in the light of changing operational requirements. The structured method proposed leads to a series of specific actions and proposals that the safety practitioner should seek to implement with colleagues in other departments within the organisation.

Critical to the efficient and effective utilisation of resources is the monitoring phase. The two areas to consider are systems management and operations management which will be looked at below.

Systems management

There must be an orderly and regular review of objectives and their implementation. The monitoring of specific objectives at critical periods is also important. Fluctuating conditions such as moratoriums on budgets, may influence schemes. If these issues are allowed to go unnoticed or unchecked then problems inevitably arise. Problems such as printing deadlines can mean lost opportunities, for example, while insufficient staff can affect other issues. Resource systems, therefore, need systematic scrutiny if programmes are to succeed. Shortfalls in the resource base should be identified at an early stage in the decision-making process and their implications should be clearly understood by the personnel manager responsible for safety. All too often a personnel manager can identify what he or she can do, but is unable to describe what he or she is unable to do and list accurately why he or she cannot do it. For example, many members of safety committees, having listened to their personnel safety managers outlining their annual report, have never asked for the results to be put into perspective or asked whether they were acceptable.

It is often assumed that safety education and training should be made available to all employees without favour or bias. Management should know whether this is happening or not and should develop a system whereby shortfalls in organisational expectations can be clearly and easily identified, and other priorities set. To quote numbers without any qualification is not good management practice.

Operational systems

Operational systems are important if projects are to meet their aims and objectives. Training schemes need to be regularly monitored if standards are to be maintained and the operational divisions of the organisations need to be contacted regularly if they are to carry out their programmes consistently and effectively. For example, if an objective is to train each and every member of middle management in a particular area once a year, then this can easily be monitored. If this objective has not been reached, then evaluation is needed to show the reasons for this failure. Likewise, if a scheme has been implemented then each stage needs discussion and regular meetings must take into account any tactical considerations.

The majority of safety practitioners do not keep accurate records of their activities. From an operational systems standpoint, information detailing each visit with dates, times, person visited etc has immense operational value. In a similar manner, details of other schemes and plans must be recorded. Some safety personnel readily accept that they do not know the extent of dangerous activities being carried out in their organisations and are unaware of the number of dangerous occurrences which happen. If the management system does not seek to quantify this information at the outset then retrospectively-based action plans need to be considered. If a stated objective of the safety unit is to acquire this information, it has to be possible to obtain it.

In terms of evaluation, there are many commercially available safety audit systems which allow personnel managers to pursue safety policies which are capable of being evaluated. Safety programme evaluation will be dealt with in detail in Chapter 8.

Although the RoSPA, the HSE and the BSC actively encourage the use of all such programmes, it is unfortunate that the topic of 'evaluation' does not feature on any of the current training courses designed for managers responsible for health and safety. Moreover, research methodology as an operational tool is similarly lacking from health and safety courses. The use of statistics does feature in a handful of courses, but these are usually academic in nature. In the accident investigation and analysis field there are even fewer opportunities to receive training. At the more basic training level, statistical methods are not covered in sufficient depth, neither are relevant examples used to illustrate them. The use of information technology and other aids to successful evaluation are sadly lacking in practice in most organisations.

Evaluation can only occur within a framework of clearly defined aims and objectives, and if undertaken by properly trained staff. Many safety professionals argue that safety activities cannot be evaluated, for example because you cannot quantify how many deaths or injuries have been avoided. This is symptomatic of this fundamental issue. Surely, if a particular plan were introduced to encourage the use of high visibility clothing in an unsupervised location, then its results could be measured. If, after the campaign, more people are found to be wearing such material than before, then some degree of success will obviously have been achieved, particularly if no such change occurred in the control group. Other areas of behaviour and attitude can be similarly evaluated. Management strategies can also be evaluated for efficiency and effectiveness.

It is recognised that specific reductions in accidents directly attributable to an education, training and/or publicity programme are very difficult to establish in terms of a simple causal relationship. Nevertheless, the safety manager's contribution to the overall corporate approach in accident reduction is now acknowledged and the long-term value of this is becoming accepted. For example, a comparison of the number of accidents in relation to the vehicle-driving population in the UK would confirm this, particularly when compared with other EC countries. The personnel manager, therefore, plays an important and vital part in this corporate plan.

In Figure 2.1 the role of the personnel manager in relation to his or her responsibilities within the context of the HASAWA is reviewed. It seems that some organisations have reacted more enthusiastically to this legislation than others. As a result, there is no standardised

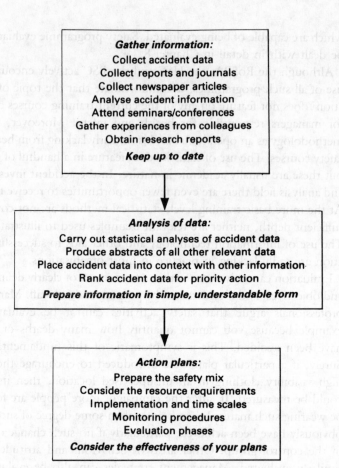

> **Gather information:**
> Collect accident data
> Collect reports and journals
> Collect newspaper articles
> Analyse accident information
> Attend seminars/conferences
> Gather experiences from colleagues
> Obtain research reports
> *Keep up to date*

> **Analysis of data:**
> Carry out statistical analyses of accident data
> Produce abstracts of all other relevant data
> Place accident data into context with other information
> Rank accident data for priority action
> *Prepare information in simple, understandable form*

> **Action plans:**
> Prepare the safety mix
> Consider the resource requirements
> Implementation and time scales
> Monitoring procedures
> Evaluation phases
> *Consider the effectiveness of your plans*

Figure 2.1 The role of the personnel manager

approach to accident reduction in the UK. Neither is there a standard recruiting policy or training provision. Safety is regarded by some top managers as a backwater in their organisation, and a role for 'problem' staff who are too old to be receptive to any substantial retraining.

Organisations must, therefore, consider a system of management that goes beyond simple public relations or law enforcement, and is actually geared towards accident prevention and reduction. This demands a different portfolio of skills. If those responsible for health and safety are to be recruited and trained for the 21st century, then is it appropriate to recruit people who are too old to undergo sustained professional retraining when compared to other younger professionals, and further, is it wise to recruit people whose personal abilities, experience and attributes are not necessarily best suited to such responsibilities? On safety at work could this be the reason why those courses which are currently available are not well attended or is this because managers responsible for recruitment and training do not really know or understand what the role of the safety professional should be?

Several safety practitioners in local government, for example, still act as instructors, and a review of recent recruitment advertisements suggests that this is what is expected. In one organisation, for example, 55% of the financial resource base was allocated to an activity occupying only 14% of the accident casualty base, yet required 64% of staff time to deal with it! In this particular company, objectives were not set, accident data were collected but not used and the safety unit carried out their duties in the same way that they had always done.

This may have been acceptable practice pre-1974, but it is now time to change. A company must operate within acceptable cost–benefit parameters. Financial restrictions dictate a tighter management approach to decision making, and safety personnel now find that they have to be even more accountable than in the past. If they cannot justify their existence, then their relative priority within the company will be diminished and their budgets will be reduced, as has already happened in some companies. Regrettably, this poor management and presentation compounds the failure of senior management fully to recognise and comprehend the actual and the potential role of those required to carry out health and safety policy and practice, to recruit the right staff and train them properly and to provide them with sufficient resources to do the job. The organisational structure may be defective. Safety is no longer the 'Cinderella' area it once was. On the contrary, it should form an integral part of the strategic plan for accident reduction and should be given appropriate priority within the organisation.

Those responsible for health and safety need to improve the information on which their decisions are based. This means that they should allocate sufficient resources to meet this requirement. Having spent time improving the quality and reliability of this primary data consideration can then be given to its analysis for decision-making purposes. From this, tactical objectives can be prepared for operational implementation and monitoring. Within this phase will be the determination of the evaluation criteria and performance indicators to be used. One of the important factors within the objective setting sequence is to quantify what cannot be achieved and to quantify more accurately why goals cannot be reached. All safety managers should develop a critical management style that provides for the identification and rectification of shortfalls. Board members, senior managers and members of safety committees should demand this information and it is right that they should be aware of all the relevant issues and not just told about what has been done. Contextual data should be used in these safety reports.

While the safety manager might consider the planning, implementation, monitoring and evaluation of the safety mix programme within specified areas of operation there are also specific tasks for which he or she would also be responsible. These are summarised in Figure 2.2.

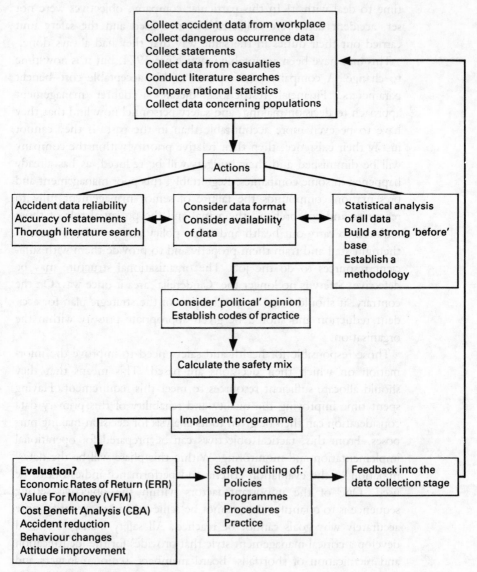

Figure 2.2 The safety management process

TAKING CARE OF SAFETY

The safety mix

The main aim of the manager responsible for health and safety should be to co-ordinate the safety mix. This forms a main feature of the remedial process and successful safety programmes are based upon a mix of some or all of the main ingredients shown in Figure 2.3. It is vary rare for one part of the mix to be successful in isolation. For example, the Department of Transport spent some £30 million attempting to persuade drivers to wear seatbelts. This was conducted via one 'E' of the safety mix, namely that involving education and publicity. It failed and a further 'E' in the form of enforcement was deemed necessary. The two elements together now account for a 96% wearing rate among car drivers. Similarly, speed limits, an enforcement requirement, are often ignored unless backed up by other measures within the safety mix framework. In the same way, the task of the safety manager is to develop an appropriate blend within the safety mix framework at local level. This aspect is usually dealt with in the programme planning stages.

Care should always be taken not to rely solely upon the enforcement aspect of the mix as the only means of providing an effective accident prevention strategy.

All these tasks must be carried out efficiently and effectively, and within clearly defined cost restraints. It is far better for the safety

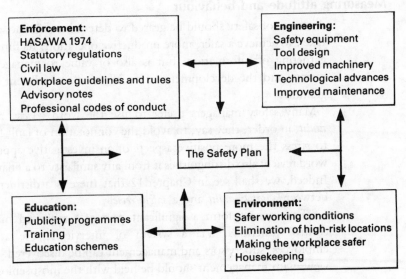

Enforcement:
HASAWA 1974
Statutory regulations
Civil law
Workplace guidelines and rules
Advisory notes
Professional codes of conduct

Engineering:
Safety equipment
Tool design
Improved machinery
Technological advances
Improved maintenance

The Safety Plan

Education:
Publicity programmes
Training
Education schemes

Environment:
Safer working conditions
Elimination of high-risk locations
Making the workplace safer
Housekeeping

Figure 2.3 The safety mix

manager to tell the accountants what is to be done rather than the other way round. In Chapter 4, we will look at some basic operations management issues which will assist the safety manager to consider various 'options' and to come to appropriate decisions.

Some notes on monitoring health and safety policy

Safety monitoring concerns an examination of procedures and programmes, the aim of which should be to help decrease the risk of accidents happening and increase productivity. A systematic approach to safety management will help the personnel manager to set objectives which will be based on priorities designed to improve management techniques, training and development, behaviour and employee attitude.

Such management practice requires some method of measuring behaviour and attitude. Measuring these is not too difficult providing both are treated positively. Positive action will produce an activity which is measurable. Good attitudes and behaviour must be developed and nurtured by management. This does not occur automatically. A genuine concern for the employee's health and safety is shown not only by management's position, but also by its action. Is management actively involved in accident prevention, or is it seen as a delegated interest? Employees are constantly evaluating the behaviour and attitude of management, and this must be seen positively from both sides.

Measuring attitude and behaviour

A review of safety should be geared to determine what action must be taken to achieve a safer, more productive operation. Its function is the gathering of information, but is also of value to management education, and the development of an effective and efficient safety programme.

Many safety managers prefer to use the word *review*, rather than *audit*, in order, they say, to avoid the connotation of fault finding and to stress the more positive aspects of an investigative approach. The word review also distinguishes it from any similarity to a financial audit. Indeed, we shall see in Chapter 12 that there is a distinct difference between a *safety audit* and a *safety review*.

Safety reviews form a significant part of established management control functions. Via a system of interviews, the attitudes of employees, supervisors and management can be discovered. Any interviews with management should be held with the most senior executive possible. Although he or she will not be able to provide detailed answers to all the questions, it is necessary to prepare well for the exercise. The reviewer or review team must provide an agenda to management in order that information can be gathered and people made available for the review.

There are advantages in obtaining external help when undertaking the first safety review. These are as follows:

- a consultant is likely to be more objective in respect to the approach, design and concluding phase than someone from within the organisation;
- they will not have any biases or be influenced by traditions;
- they will not be influenced by personalities;
- independence can be very effective when changes are recommended.

The size and membership of the safety review team will largely depend on the complexity of the facility involved and the expertise that is required. It will be necessary to have periodic reviews every two to three years done by an external expert, particularly if there are many changes in the organisation or operation.

Review methodology

It is important to discuss the practicalities of the review process required to assist group executives and location management in the development or evaluation of their accident prevention activities. The areas for consideration listed below outline the general topics required for discussion with senior management. A comprehensive safety review requires that it be conducted by safety practitioners who will draw from their knowledge and experience so that useful information can be obtained. There are five review elements:

- administration;
- accident investigation and analysis processes;
- job analysis;
- self-inspection;
- contingency planning.

In addition to these elements, which are discussed further below, a number (the larger the sample the better will be the results) of supervisors and employees should be picked at random and interviewed to assess their safety attitude and to obtain data concerning their perception of the safety programme. It is important to select these people by occupation or trade rather than by name. This then removes, as far as possible, any prejudices for or against management or its programmes.

A review should start with a conference with senior management in order to explain the agenda and to answer any questions that may arise. The exercise should end with an exit interview so that any recommendations can be fully explained and any differences resolved prior to the final report being published. Where an internal review is conducted, the team should obtain a conclusive response from senior management for each recommendation made. The scope of a rigorous safety review should be to evaluate the five elements listed above in the following ways.

ADMINISTRATION

The interest of management and their full participation are the most important factors in any safety review activity. It is important to maintain this situation and secure management involvement. Managers must be visible in the workplace for the promotion of safety as well as for production. In this way, it is possible to unite these two concepts to ensure safe production.

In a complex industrial or mining operation, there are often several facilities tied to an administrative or headquarters-type location. Individual sites sometimes have little or no control over areas of programmes or systems governing their operations, particularly those set up for the whole organisation. Examples might include the safety programme outline, the disciplinary programme or the needs of the workforce. It is important, therefore, that locations are evaluated for those systems which they control and that headquarters-type centres are analysed for those that they command in the following ways.

Headquarters or group

- describe the loss control programme for employees, processes, contractors and equipment.
- What is the senior manager's role in the accident prevention programme?
- Is there a safety manager and to whom is he or she responsible?
- How often is the accident prevention programme reviewed internally for effectiveness?
- Is there a programme for training supervisors based on established need?
- Does senior management occasionally attend site safety meetings?
- Is there a system which recognises supervisors' and employees' safety achievement?
- Are aims and objectives required for safety performance?

- Are objectives realistic and measurable?
- Are objectives measured?
- What consideration is given to matching (wo)man, machine, and the environment in the hiring and placement of employees?
- Outline the programme for the selection and purchase of facilities, equipment processes and protective clothing and equipment.

Site or satellite location

- Outline the accident prevention programme for employees, processes, contractors and equipment.
- What is the role of management in the safety programme?
- Does management recognise supervisors and employees for their safety achievement?
- Does management initiate procedural and motivational communications to staff?
- Does management participate in accident prevention inspections of the facility?
- Does management attend occasional safety meetings with the workforce?
- Are safety aims and objectives set jointly by the entire management team at that location?
- Are the objectives measured?
- Does senior management review all major incidents and subsequent statistical analyses?
- Is there a preventive maintenance programme?
- Is there a system of selection and placement of employees?
- Is there a job analysis programme in operation?
- Outline the training programme for management development and supervisory safety task training.
- Is there a safety co-ordinator and what are his, or her responsibilities?

ACCIDENT AND DANGEROUS OCCURRENCE INVESTIGATION

- Are all incidents, including those requiring first-aid, investigated for type and contributory factors?
- Do remedial measures attack the factors contributing to the incident happening?
- What system is used to follow up on preventive measures?
- Does the investigation indicate the potential for severity?
- Are all fatalities, major injuries and illnesses, and high-cost incidents investigated?

- Does each department head review all incidents in his or her department?
- Does the safety department review and follow up on all incident reports?
- Are thorough analyses made of all incidents for trends? Are these analyses reviewed by senior management?
- Is there a method of determining the number and type of incidents resulting in lost time from off-the-job injuries and illnesses?
- Are off-the-job incidents analysed for type and costs to the facility? Are these analyses communicated to senior management?
- Do employee safety awareness programmes include off-the-job safety?
- Is off-the-job safety information provided to the families of employees?

JOB ANALYSIS

- Has a priority list of hazardous or high-risk jobs been established?
- Are hazardous/high risk jobs analysed by method to determine the potential for accident and the safe work procedure?
- Are the priority listed jobs necessary to accomplish the work aims?
- Who participates in the job analysis?
- Is job or task training based on the completed job analysis?
- Are safe work procedures, developed through job analyses?
- Are they used as guides by employees to perform work, by supervisors to train and supervise, or by managers to manage?
- Are the job analyses reviewed when incidents occur, there is a change in equipment, there is a change in environment, or there is a change in the process?
- Are equipment pre-use or inspection check sheets developed using the job analysis procedure?
- Are tags and signs developed and used to support the safe work procedures?

SELF-INSPECTION

- Is there an inspection team with representation from management, production, safety and employees?
- Does the team have a checklist including all areas of the facility?

- Is there a system of follow up for the remedy of unsafe conditions and practices observed?
- Does the inspection include the preventive maintenance programme records?

In addition to the overall plant inspection, are periodic inspections made:

- By department heads and supervisors of individual areas?
- By a safety practitioner?
- By senior management?

CONTINGENCY PLANNING

- How many emergency medically qualified personnel are there on each shift?
- How many are trained in first-aid?
- Where are the first-aid stations located?

Table 2.2 *A personnel manager's health and safety checklist*

Task	Response
Who is in charge of the job?	
Has anyone else a responsibility for the job?	
Can you identify any task which nobody is responsible for?	
Are there established safe ways of doing the job?	
What are the guidance notes or codes of practice?	
Have you provided safe working procedures to do the job?	
Do you need to make the job safe?	
Do workers need protective clothing?	
Do workers know the limitation of safety equipment and clothing?	
Has anyone assessed the equipment to be used in terms of suitability?	
What will be the consequences if it goes wrong?	
Does the person in charge know what to do if things go wrong?	
Can emergency services get to the site?	
If the job cannot be finished today can it be left in a safe state?	
Are there clear enough instructions for the next shift?	
Does everyone else know what is going on?	
Has the job been done in the way intended?	
Has anyone checked it?	

- How often are the first-aid stations checked for operational efficiency?
- Is there a doctor on retainer or designated?
- Are there clear written emergency and communication procedures?
- Are the responsibilities of management and supervisors clearly defined in these procedures?
- What is the availability of ambulance services if required?
- Who administers or co-ordinates the emergency procedures?

A safety review places emphasis and encourages activity where it will produce the best results. Management and supervision are key factors in effective safety programmes. It is the responsibility of the safety manager to ensure that such reviews are held regularly and that the whole workforce, including senior management, are involved. It is positive action, rather than what is said, which is of vital importance in demonstrating the position of management.

TAKING CARE OF SAFETY

CHAPTER 3
Health and Safety Policy

Various measures can be taken to prevent accidents, but when they do happen you need to be prepared, and in this chapter we look at disaster and emergency plans. We shall also cover statements of health and safety policy, safety representatives and committees and how to deal with accidents and dangerous occurrences. The special needs of women workers are discussed, and we finish with an examination of industrial tribunals.

Disasters and emergency plans

To prevent accidents from occurring, there are a series of laws and voluntary strategies which can be implemented cheaply and effectively. This book and the publications suggested in the section *Further reading* suggest ways in which various accident prevention and reduction strategies can be planned, implemented, monitored and evaluated. A disaster is no different and will thus be preventable using the same principles and practice. However, there are varying degrees of disaster ranging from the straightforward, typical workplace accident to one which can cause the workplace to cease trading completely or cause great harm to people and property outside the immediate vicinity of the incident. It is this latter type of incident which will be considered here. Very few organisations possess an emergency plan which can quickly be brought into operation and the intention here is to prompt personnel managers to seek the appropriate advice by obtaining answers to the following questions.

- do you have a criteria set out which describes clearly what would be a disaster to your company?
- Do you have a procedure to contain the disaster?

- Do you have plans to enable the company to continue trading?
- Do you have a building evacuation procedure?
- Are appropriate personnel trained in your emergency procedures?
- Have you tested your emergency plans?
- Are your plans adequate?
- Have you publicised your prevention policies, procedures and practice to the workforce?

The most common type of disaster likely to occur is a fire and fire procedures will be covered in more detail in Chapter 5.

It must be remembered that although adequate insurance may be held by an organisation, it must have some plans to continue trading safely in the event of a disaster occurring. Insurance alone is not enough.

Statements of health and safety policy

One of the legal provisions of section 2 of the HASAWA requires employers who employ five people or more to prepare, and keep up to date, a written statement of their policy regarding the health and safety of their employees.

Your policy may consist of one complete manual or it may be a compilation of several individual documents relating to particular areas of your activity. Whatever form it takes it should comprise three separate and distinct parts covering:

- general statement of policy;
- organisation and responsibilities for carrying out the policy;
- arrangements for ensuring safety and health of employees.

Many organisations produce a general statement of intent and require individual departments, cost centres or directorates to develop safety policies which appropriately reflect the day-to-day activities of the department.

By looking through the policy you should find an indication that the organisation will provide resources for health and safety along with the provision of safe plant and equipment, safe systems of work, training for staff and supervision. In fact, you should observe a resemblance to the general duties laid down by section 2 of the HASAWA.

As far as responsibilities are concerned, these should include the duties of employees at all levels in the organisation.

General statement of policy

Here you should state the company's policy in respect of:

- provision and maintenance of safe and healthy working conditions;
- equipment and safe systems of work for all employees;
- provision of health and safety information, training and supervision necessary;
- a statement regarding the acceptance of responsibility for the health and safety of other people who may be affected by your activities.

Within this section, it is good practice to outline the allocation of duties for all safety matters and the particular arrangements which will be made to implement your company health and safety policy. Your statement of health and safety policy should always reflect the changes in nature and size of the company, and as such be kept up to date. To ensure this, personnel managers responsible for health and safety matters within their organisations should see to it that such statements are reviewed every year and amended accordingly.

Organisation and responsibilities for carrying out the policy

This section should cover those general arrangements for the carrying out of health and safety policy such as:

- procedures for the reporting and recording of accidents and dangerous occurrences;
- location of first-aid boxes;
- details of all qualified first-aid personnel;
- details of fire procedures;
- fire extinguisher location and maintenance details;
- fire alarm location and maintenance details;
- fire routines and testing arrangements;
- medical and health care arrangements;
- safety training details including specialist training;
- discipline and codes of conduct;
- advice for visitors and/or contractors.

Arrangements for ensuring safety and health of employees

This final section should list details about all potential hazards in the workplace. These should be listed so that everyone is aware of them. If you use hazardous substances, then the manufacturer will provide hazard sheets, while the Health and Safety Executive (HSE) will provide additional advice if it is required. Make sure that the workforce is aware of all hazards. This section should also provide information concerning:

- cleanliness of the premises;
- waste disposal details;
- details concerning safe stacking and storage;
- marking and maintaining clear walkways and exits;
- equipment-checking procedures;
- details concerning access to restricted areas;
- routines for checking electrical appliances;
- routines for the reporting of faults;
- rules regarding the use of extension cables and portable equipment;
- arrangements with electrical and or equipment contractors;
- rules concerning the use of all machinery;
- details of routine maintenance and timetables;
- dangerous substance details;
- protective equipment and clothing information;
- routines for storing, handling and disposal of dangerous substances;
- operation, use and maintenance of compressed air equipment;
- storage, labelling and use of compressed gases and or fluids;
- procedures regarding water pressure and/or steam;
- in-house rules and regulations about the use of internal transport, use and care of protective equipment and clothing, noise, maintenance of appliances, and any other special hazards in your company.

It is good practice to include a company's health and safety policy (see Figure 3.1 for a sample policy) in the induction course programme for new employees.

Safety representatives and committees

A safety representative is an employee nominated by his or her trade union to represent colleagues in discussions with the employer on matters relating to health and safety at work. He or she may carry out surveys or inspections of the workplace with the object of identifying hazards or potential dangers. Employers are required to disclose to such representatives all information necessary for them to carry out their duties and functions. Details of the necessary information can be found in paragraph 6 of the Approved Code of Practice on Safety Representatives and Safety Committees. At the same time, health and

Health and Safety at Work Act 1974

+---+
| This is the policy of: |
| **ABC Manufacturing Ltd** |
| Weymouth Avenue New Town Barchester BB1 1AA |
+---+

Dear employee

Health and Safety Policy

You will know from your contract of employment that you are an employee of ABC Manufacturing Ltd whose health and safety policy applies to you under the Health and Safety at Work Act 1974.

This document contains a copy of that safety policy and the statement of organisation and other arrangements adopted by the company to implement it.

These documents set out the procedures which management will apply in the interests of the health and safety of all employees. It is our wish to emphasise that each and every one of us has a duty to take reasonable care of ourselves and those of our fellow workers.

We must all work together to prevent accidents happening and the hardship that they cause.

Yours sincerely

Chairman (or Managing Director)   January 1992

This introduction may be in the form of a letter or company headed paper to each employee together with the policy document or bound in as an integral part of the document.

Figure 3.1 A sample health and safety policy document
(pages 86–100)

Health and Safety at Work Act 1974
The purpose of this document is to set out the Health and Safety Policy of **ABC Manufacturing Ltd** as required by section 2(3) of the Health and Safety at Work Act 1974.

General policy
It is the policy of ABC Manufacturing Ltd:

1. to safeguard the health, safety and welfare of all its employees while at work, and to provide, so as far is reasonably practicable, working environments which are safe and without risk to health;

2. to conduct its undertakings in such a way as to ensure, so far as is reasonably practicable, that people not in its employment, but who may be affected, are not exposed to risks to their health and safety;

3. to recognise its obligations to meet all relevant legislative requirements pertaining to health and safety which apply to any of the company's undertakings; and

4. to organise and arrange the company affairs to ensure compliance with this policy.

In carrying out this policy it is the practice of ABC Manufacturing:

1. to specify in writing managerial responsibility and accountability for the health, safety and welfare of its employees, and for the health and safety of others who may be affected by the company undertaking;

2. to ensure that appropriate safety training and instruction is provided on the introduction of new and/or unfamiliar methods and equipment, and that accident prevention is included in all relevant training programmes, especially those for apprentices, young trainees, new members of staff and other employees;

3. by a programme of regular propaganda and other appropriate measures, ensure an awareness of the need to prevent accidents and risks to health in the minds of employees;

4. to take into account, when planning its work, any aspects which will help eliminate injury, industrial disease, pollution and waste;

5. to make appropriate accident prevention arrangements at the place of work and maintain liaison with all other employers who have employees working at the same location; and

6. to encourage the discussion of health and safety matters at all levels within the company, including the setting up of arrangements for joint consultation with employees, through their appointed safety representatives.

Health and Safety at Work Act 1974

The company recognises that it has a legal requirement to bring to the notice of all its employees its health and safety policy.

The company will maintain contact with the Health and Safety Executive (HSE), its own consultants and other groups in order to keep itself informed about health and safety matters. It also recognises that there exists a large body of authoritative documentation in the form of legislation, approved codes of practice, HSE guidance notes, HSE publications and British Standards. ABC Manufacturing will establish and maintain an index of all such relevant publications so that they may be readily identified by the company and its employees.

Responsibilities:

Overall responsibility for health and safety in ABC Manufacturing Ltd is with:

Mr Albert Bloggs, Managing Director

Responsibility for the implementation and monitoring of this policy is with:

Mrs Betty Lepew, Works Manager

In the absence of the works manager the person below is responsible:

Mr James Turner

The following supervisors are responsible for health and safety in specific areas:

Mrs Alice Springs	Finishing Room
Mr Mal Coombe	Tool Room
Mrs Irene Box	Despatch
Mr Uriah Heap	Stores
Mrs Felicity Harper-Brown	Sales
Mrs Jane Scudd	Administration

All employees have the responsibility to co-operate with managers and supervisors to achieve a healthy and safe workplace and to take reasonable steps to care for themselves and others.

If you notice a health and safety problem, and cannot rectify the matter then you must inform one of the persons whose names are shown above as soon as possible.

Consultation between management and employees is provided by:

Mr Fred Smallpiece
National Union of Widget Tappers

The following staff are responsible for:

Safety training	Mrs Wendy Baggs
Safety inspections	Mr Runjit Patel
Accident investigation	Mrs Wendy Baggs
Safety maintenance	Mr James Dyen

First-aid boxes are sited at:

Finishing room
Tool room
Despatch
Stores
Sales
Administration

Those responsible for their first-aid boxes are the following qualified first-aiders:

Finishing room   Winston Bakerlight
Tool room   Crispin Smith
Despatch   Tom Cobley
Stores   Anne Seagrove
Sales   Alison Baker-Brown
Administration   Mary Grimshaw

Mrs I of Administration is the Company Fire Officer. Her telephone number is

Ext 4550

Mrs I is responsible for evacuation procedures and for the maintenance of all fire equipment. She from time to time (at least once per month) tests the fire alarms. Escape routes and assembly points are clearly shown on the diagram displayed on the notice board in your work area.

Hosepipes and extinguishers are maintained by:

Firehose and Fire Extinguishers Ltd
New Town
Barchester BB3 3AC

Tel: 0333 123

Smoke detectors are maintained by:

Smoke Detectors Ltd
New Town
Barchester BB2 6AJ

Tel: 0333 121

KEEP ESCAPE ROUTES CLEAR

This company employs the following person as a safety consultant:

R A Blogg MSc, PhD, MIIRSM
Bloggs Safety and Health Ltd
New Town
Barchester BH2 2EZ

The Company Doctor is:

Dr J Smith MB, BCh, MRCP
The Surgery
New Town
Barchester BB1 1TY

The Company Nurse is:

Ms Gladys Emmanuelle RGN
The Surgery
New Town
Barchester BB1 1TY

Health and safety training is provided by:

Barchester Safety Training Services Ltd
The Industrial Estate
New Town
Barchester BB3 3LL

The following jobs are hazardous and must not be undertaken without specialist training:

Tool tapping
Blank blasting
Sheet shearing

These jobs use chemicals and equipment which, if wrongly used, can cause severe accidents and ill-health. See your supervisor for specialist training arrangements.

(Outline the procedures to be followed by contractors and visitors below.)

Rules for contractors:

_____

_____

Rules for visitors:

_____

TAKING CARE OF SAFETY

(List below the number and types of hazard which you may need to provide for. Set out the rules.)

_____

Hazard sheets:

_____

_____

Manufacturer's guidance:

_____

_____

Other guidance:

_____

_____

House rules:

_____

(For housekeeping purposes you will need to list the areas of concern and include the rules involved.)

Cleanliness (buildings):

_____

_____

Cleanliness (personal):

_____

_____

Waste disposal:

_____

_____

Safe staking and storage:

_____

_____

Marking and keeping clear gangways, and exits:

_____

_____

Checking of equipment and access to special places:

_____

_____

(Electrical equipment will require regular maintenance and checking.
State below.)

Routines for the inspection of plugs, cables, loose connections
and faults:

Rules for using extension cables and portable equipment:

Periodic check arrangements with contractors and/or suppliers:

(Rules covering the use of all machinery must be set out below.)

Rules for the use of:

Tool tapper

Blank blaster

Sheet shearer

Equipment type:	Who should check it	When should it be checked
Tool tapper	Lionel Wilson	Daily before each shift
Blank blaster	Abdul Rashid	Weekly
Sheet shearer	Alan Jones	Once per month

(Rules concerning the use of dangerous substances should be listed below.)

(Rules concerning pressurised fluids and their use.)

(You may need additional rules to cover such matters as:
Internal transport
use and care of protective equipment and clothing
ventilation
noise
use of VDUs
temperature
lighting
maintenance of appliances and other hazards connected with your
particular business.)

_____

Hazards:

_____

_____

Rules:

_____

_____

Maintenance:

_____

(You may need additional rules to cover such matters as:

alcohol advice
drugs and medicines
welfare issues (such as sports facilities and personal counselling).)

_____

Rules concerning alcohol and general advice:

_____

_____

Advice concerning the use of drugs and medications whilst carrying out certain tasks:

_____

_____

Welfare issues:

Counselling and advice:

Other welfare issues such as sporting and leisure facilities:

_____

(Finally, you may also need rules and advice in relation to road safety such as:

car parking arrangements
speed limits on works roadways
advice on entering and leaving the works
restricted parking areas
pedestrian walkways
works vehicles
general road safety advice.)

Rules concerning vehicle use:

Parking arrangements:

Security:

Advice concerning own vehicle:

Advice when using works vehicles:

Pedestrian walkways:

General road safety advice:

---

safety inspectors are also required to provide safety representatives with technical information obtained as a result of a visit to their workplace. This must include details of prosecutions, improvement notices, prohibition orders, and any correspondence with the employer on health and safety matters. All action considered by an inspector as the result of a visit must be discussed with the safety representative.

As far as the personnel manager is concerned, the safety representative(s) within an organisation are an extremely valuable asset. They must be met with regularly, involved directly within the decision-making process and considered to be an extension of the overall health and safety programme.

For safety committees to be effective they must not be too large, otherwise their ability to make decisions effectively is diminished. They must be made up of senior management, trade union safety representatives, with the secretariat being provided by the safety manager or one of his or her members of staff. Chairmanship of the committee should follow normal electoral procedures and a constitution should allow for periodical changes to the structure to take place. Decisions taken by the committee must be adhered to and carried out as soon as is reasonably practicable. Merely having a safety committee because the regulations say you have been requested to have one is a severe waste of resources if it is not permitted to make an effective contribution to the overall well-being of the organisation.

Decisions concerning new laws and regulations affecting working practices should be placed before the safety committee for discussion. From this, all matters concerning the planning, implementation, monitoring and evaluation of policy may be discussed openly and widely.

These regulations came into force on 1 October 1978 and gave trade unions the right to appoint safety representatives to perform the following functions:

- to investigate potential hazards and dangerous occurrences at the workplace and to examine the cause of accidents;
- to investigate complaints by employees in relation to health, safety and welfare at work and to make representations to the employer on these issues;
- to take up general matters of health and safety at work and to represent employees in consultation with HSE inspectors;
- to attend meetings of the safety committee when and if necessary;
- to carry out a workplace inspection every three months after

giving reasonable notice to the employer of intention to do so;

- to carry out workplace inspections (after consultation with his or her employers) when there has been a change in conditions of work, or new information has been issued concerning relevant hazards. The employer is entitled to be represented at these inspections if he or she wishes.

The idea of workers being involved in these activities has been debated for many years and was actually resisted by many trade unions because they suspected that their involvement might relieve employers of some of their responsibility for health and safety.

It is important to note, therefore, that the activities outlined above are merely functions which the representative may carry out. They do not relieve the employer of any responsibility whatsoever and do not confer any legal liability on the appointed representative.

The regulations specify a number of other provisions relating to the training of safety representatives and the provision of information relating to safety and health at work. An organisation's safety policy may specify the local arrangements to be made to enable safety representatives to perform these functions.

Safety representatives are an important influence in the provision and maintenance of a safe and healthy working environment.

Accidents and dangerous occurrences

The requirement to report injuries, diseases and dangerous occurrences is contained in the Reporting of Injuries, Diseases and Dangerous Occurrences Regulations 1985 (RIDDOR). These regulations require that when any of the following events occur, the responsible person must report the event in writing to the enforcing authority and must keep a record of it. The regulations also stress that the responsible person should notify the enforcing authority by telephone as soon as is reasonably practicable where:

- a death occurs to any person, whether or not he or she is at work, as the result of an accident arising out of or in connection with work;
- any person suffers a specified major injury or condition as a result of an accident arising out of or in connection with work;
- one of a list of specified dangerous occurrences arising out of or in connection with work happens;

- a person at work is incapacitated for his or her normal work for more than three days as a result of an injury caused by an accident at work;
- the death of an employee occurs some time after a reportable injury which led to that employee's death, but not more than one year afterwards; or
- a person at work is affected by one of a number of specified diseases, provided that a medical practitioner diagnoses the disease and that the person's job involves a specified work activity.

The procedure to be followed is illustrated in Figure 3.2.

When making a report, it is necessary to complete Form 2508 (revised January 1986) for the reporting of deaths, injuries and dangerous occurrences, and Form 2508A should be used when reporting cases of disease.

The regulations also require employers to keep records of every event which has caused injury, however small, or which has the potential to cause injury. The details to be kept are as follows:

- date and time of the accident or dangerous occurrence;
- details of the person(s) affected and including
  - full name(s)
  - occupation(s)
  - nature of the injury or condition;

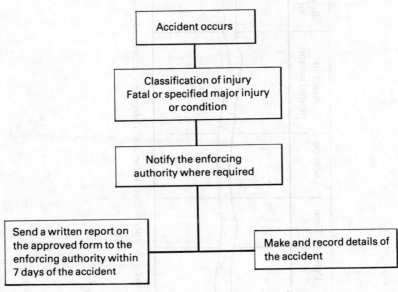

Figure 3.2 How to report and record accidents which happen

Date	Time	Location	Name of injured person	Brief description of the accident	Action taken	By whom action taken

Figure 3.3 Internal accident and dangerous occurrence summary sheet

ABC Manufacturing Ltd　　　　　　　　　Ref number ☐

Name ☐　　　　　　　　　　　　　　　　Age ☐

Address ☐　　　　　　　　　　　　　　　Works number ☐

　　　　　　　　　　　　　　　　　　　Employed as ☐

　　　　　Post code　　　　　　　　　　Date commenced ☐

STATEMENT – concerning the accident

Date of accident ☐　　Time of accident ☐　　Number of people involved ☐

Location of accident ☐

Details of injuries received ☐　　Was this a fatal accident? YES/NO

Is this the statement of:　THE CASUALTY/WITNESS?

Statement:

Continue on a separate sheet if necessary

Figure 3.4　Witness or casualty record sheet

- location where the accident or occurrence took place;
- a brief description of the incident.

In addition, where a disease is concerned, the following information will need to be recorded:

- date of diagnosis;
- personal details of affected person;
- name and nature of the disease.

All records must be kept for three years and be made available to the enforcing authority if or when required. There is flexibility in the way records may be kept provided that they contain the above particulars. Sample forms are shown in Figures 3.3 and 3.4.

Liability insurance

It is a statutory requirement for most companies in the UK to have an insurance policy which provides cover against claims for injury and/or disease by employees. When a policy is taken out, the insurers provide a certificate of insurance which the employer must display in a prominent position at the worksite, where employees and anyone else requiring to see it can do so.

Failure to effect and maintain valid insurance for any day on which it is required is a criminal offence as is failure to display a valid certificate of insurance.

The object of having such insurance is to make certain that employers are covered for any legal liability to pay damages to employees who are injured or caused ill-health through their employment. Such a policy protects an employer from third-party claims but not for non-employees. Where contractors or members of the public are concerned it is necessary to take out additional insurance, referred to as public liability insurance. While such a policy might be desirable it is not a legal requirement. All statutory liability insurance must be available under one or more approved policies. These policies are not subject to any conditions or exception prohibited by the law.

An employer is not required to insure against liability to an employee who is:

- a father;
- a mother;
- a son or daughter;
- a wife or husband;
- a close relative.

With regard to the degree of cover necessary, it is a requirement to maintain insurance of £2,000,000, but most reputable insurance companies impose no upper limit.

Exempted employers are:

- local authorities;
- civil service;
- nationalised bodies;
- commission for the new towns;
- statutory water authorities;
- London transport.

Women workers

There are many books available which cover the Sex Discrimination Act 1975 in detail (see Appendix 3, Further Reading List, Chapter 1), and it is not intended to recover this ground here. In terms of health and safety, however, case law has shown that a woman's health and safety in certain circumstances takes precedence over a duty not to discriminate. For example, in the case of *Page v Freight Hire (Tank Haulage) Ltd* [1981] IRLR 13, a 23-year-old woman was employed as a heavy goods vehicle driver of tankers carrying the chemical dimethylformamide (DMF). On a recommendation from ICI that women of child-bearing age should not be employed in driving lorries loaded with the chemical DMF, Mrs Page was taken off this kind of work. She brought a claim of unlawful sex discrimination.

The decision in the case did not allow an employer to stop employing women as soon as a hint of danger arose. What had to be considered was the employer's duty under section 2 of the HASAWA. In this particular case, evidence from the manufacturer was that the chemical was dangerous to women of Mrs Page's age, and, therefore, the steps taken to remove her from the danger were reasonable. There was, therefore, no unlawful discrimination.

The effect of the Sex Discrimination Acts of 1975 and 1986 has been to remove some of the restrictions on women in relation to their work but restrictions and prohibitions on certain types of employment are still in force in the interests of health and safety.

Industrial tribunals

Industrial relations is a multi-disciplinary subject, the content of which is controversial. This is not surprising because the employment relationship is a complex economic relationship which takes place within a social, psychological, political and cultural context, expressed legally by each individual contract of employment. The background to this relationship is often a complicated pattern of shifting forces and changing environments, public pressures, private fears, world markets, weekly household bills, driving ambitions and security. The issues involved with industrial relations arise out of the questions of who does what, who gets what, and what is fair, in relation to income, treatment and time, and all these questions provide potential for the emergence of conflict.

Income

Aspects of income which are often regarded as unfair:

- between the low paid and the rest;
- between earned and unearned income
- between wages, staff salaries and fringe benefits;
- between occupations and between industries;
- between grades and internal differentials;
- between public and private sector;
- between jobs in different regions;
- wage system not reflecting the changing aspirations of the staff;
- company not accommodating technical change;
- not enabling changes in marketing and sales policies.

Treatment

Are the needs and expectations of the modern industrial worker being catered for in respect of:

- fringe benefits;
- staff status;
- facilities?

Management needs organisation, but workers respond best as individuals or as informal working groups. While management might initiate change, the worker may only be interested in job security.

Time

Management should consider the following.

- Is overtime necessary?
- What about shift work, the conflict between man and machine?

- What of stress?
- And bonus schemes?

The time factor has been identified as having a strong association with accident causation.

Rule-making processes

There are a number of rule-making processes regulating the employment relationship. The purpose of rules, both formal and informal, is to establish rights and obligations which together outline spheres of authority and define status, and thus establish norms of expected and appropriate behaviour. The main rules and rule-making processes concerning the employment relationship are:

- legislation;
- collective bargaining;
- unilateral management decisions;
- unilateral trade union regulations;
- the individual contract of employment;
- custom and practice;
- arbitration awards both voluntary and statutory;
- social conventions.

So, as well as the issue of fairness providing potential for conflict, so do aspects of the rule-making processes. The following questions should be asked.

- Who should make the rules and how?
- What is the appropriate process?
- What issues should the rules cover?
- How are the rules to be implemented?
- How are the rules to be enforced?
- How are the rules changed?
- How are the rules to be legitimised by those affected?
- What are the effects of new rules on existing managerial prerogatives?

There are basically two types of rule, namely:

- **substantive rules** which include rules governing compensation, rules regulating duties, expected performance and discipline matters. They also cover rules defining rights and duties of employees;
- **procedural rules** which are concerned with defining the procedures for the establishment and administration of substantive rules.

In essence, substantive rules define jobs, while procedural rules regulate the defining process. Job evaluation is of use in getting agreement about what is regarded as being fair in order to assess:

- skill and training requirements;
- the social worth of the job;
- the physical effort required;
- the level of experience and competence required;
- the level of responsibility;
- the level of danger and risk.

Factors also relevant to this issue are:

- ability and age;
- working life expectancy of the job;
- ability of the employer to pay;
- productivity;
- persistence, honesty and reliability;
- scarcity value;
- social needs and traditions.

Where conflict occurs there must be a means of resolving the matter quickly and safely. If the matter cannot be resolved internally, industrial tribunals have been set up to consider cases where independent arbitration is necessary. They were originally intended to deal with disputes quickly, cheaply and informally in order to deal with injustices in the employment sphere. The industrial tribunal is made up of a panel of three persons of which the chairman is usually the only one who is legally qualified. While there is no requirement to be represented by a legal expert, employment law is so complicated that it is often recommended that legal representation or legal aid be provided. Where an employee is a member of a trade union it is usual for the trade union to represent their client.

The make up of a tribunal usually consists of one trade union panel member, one employer and the chairman who ensures that the complexities of the law are interpreted and followed. For a decision to be reached, a tribunal needs a majority view. Decisions may only be challenged if:

- the decision discloses an error on the part of the tribunal;
- a party did not receive notice of proceedings;
- a decision was reached in the absence of a party entitled to be heard;
- new evidence has come to light;
- the interests of justice require a review.

The chairman can refuse an application for a review if he believes it will be unsuccessful. Applications for reviews must normally be made within 14 days of the decision of the tribunal being made known.

Industrial tribunals are empowered to hear complaints under the following Acts:

- Equal Pay Act 1970
- Health and Safety at Work Act 1974
- Sex Discrimination Act 1975
- Trade Union and Labour Relations Act 1976
- Race Relations Act 1976
- Employment Protection (Consolidation) Act 1978
- Employment Act 1980
- Employment Act 1982
- Sex Discrimination Act 1986

and subsequent similar legislation.

Some examples of health and safety matters which may be heard include:

- failure of an employer to pay safety representatives for time off for carrying out duties and for training;
- failure of an employer to make a medical suspension payment;
- appeals against improvement and prohibition notices;
- dismissal, whether actual or constructive, following a breach of health and safety law, regulation or term of an employment contract.

Appeals are made against improvement notices and prohibition notices on the following grounds:

- the substantive law involved; or
- time limits for compliance.

CHAPTER 4
Accident Investigation

In this chapter we shall be looking at how to gather accident and other relevant information, sources of data and primary and secondary information. We also look at how to collect accident data, gathering information from people and concluding formal interviews.

Gathering accident and other relevant information

Studies have found that some organisations keep no accident or dangerous occurrence records other than those provided for in Form F2508. Many do not computerise their data, but continue to maintain expensive and cumbersome manual systems. Data collection by some companies is seen as merely meeting the requirements of statutory obligations and few exploit the value of such costly information as a management tool.

Other researchers have found that people are more likely to forget facts and may not be able to recall up to half of what they originally perceived when questioned as little as 24 hours after the event. Gathering good, reliable information must be a part of the role of the personnel manager or indeed any manager and not necessarily only for use in disciplinary matters. While the casualty might be excused from recalling certain information about an accident through shock, it is important that procedures are in place which ensure that witnesses are spoken to within 24 hours whenever possible, and that the interview is structured correctly.

Published information from the HSE is not enough to assist the personnel manager in programme planning. It lacks sufficient detail and contributory factors are not identified in sufficient depth to assist with the identification of trends. Once contributory factors are identified then appropriate remedial measures can be introduced using the safety mix referred to in Chapter 2, ie by enforcement, education, engineering, environmental strategies or a mix of some or all four. Making something illegal will not prevent it from happening and there will always be a need to combine enforcement with one or more of the other factors or elements within the safety mix.

Because of poor information gathering, a large number of safety management decisions are based upon opinion. In order to get the most accurate information, there are six basic categories of question that should be asked after all accidents.

Who?

- Who was involved in the accident?
- Who was the line manager responsible for safety?
- Who reported the accident?
- Who was called to respond to the accident?
- Who was notified?
- Who should have been notified?
- Who was responsible?

When?

- When did the accident occur?
- When were people aware that an accident could occur?
- When did help arrive at the scene of the accident?

Why?

- Why did the accident happen?
- Why were safety practices not applied?
- Why did safety procedures fail to work?

What?

- What actually happened?
- What were the losses incurred?
- What injuries were sustained?
- What could have been done to avoid the occurrence?

Where?

- Where did the accident occur?
- Where was the safety officer or line manager at the time of the accident?

How?

- How did the event occur? Rapidly, slowly, without warning?
- How could safety procedures and practices have been improved?
- How can the organisation learn from the accident occurrence?

Research studies have identified human errors and failings as contributing, with other factors, to the vast majority of accidents and dangerous occurrences. Failing to cope with circumstances leading up to and prevailing at the time of the accident will be evident in most situations. It is important that all accident investigations consider human error and it is therefore vital to identify prime factors involving human behaviour as a major part of the accident investigation, together with human reaction to unsafe conditions within the workplace.

The two primary objectives of accident investigation are as follows.

- **Accident reduction** By obtaining sufficient data to facilitate the systematic reduction in the type and severity of accidents in the workplace and implementing the safety mix by providing information of sufficient quality to balance the mix to best effect.
- **Accident prevention** This relates to the application of safety principles in new design and technology, whether in the area of automation or improvements to the style and type of manufacturing methodology employed in the workplace.

Both these strategies must be based upon recognised opportunities available to the designer, engineer, enforcer or general safety practitioner for influencing and preventing all forms of accidents from happening. Both strategies require the co-operation of everyone in the company to succeed and must not be left to one person to solve alone. Only in this way can effective strategies be employed.

It is important that the safety representative is involved in all accident investigations and that he or she is fully aware of the aims and objectives of the data collection process. It must be appreciated that in certain circumstances accurate data collection can be hampered by the 'high status' phenomenon (in other words, investigation from above) and care must be exercised so that the investigation is not seen as a purely disciplinary or enforcement procedure. Such investigations may assist in the formulation of rules and safe procedures, but should not

A. Subject of Report:

Fatality ☐ | Specified major injury ☐ | 3 day injury ☐ | Dangerous occurrence ☐ | Flammable gas incident ☐ | Dangerous gas fitting ☐

1 · 2 · 3 · 4 · 5 · 6

B. Person or Organisation Making the Report:

Name and address

Type of business

Role of company at time

Post code ☐   Main site contractor ☐   Sub-contractor ☐   Other ☐

Name & telephone number of contact

Is injured member of your family? ☐ Yes ☐ No

C. Date, Time and Place of Accident or Incident:

Day Month Year

Time of accident

24-hour clock

Location of accident

Normal activity carried out at site

D. The Injured Person:

Name & address

Age ☐   Sex ☐   Employee ☐   Trainee ☐   Self-employed ☐   YTS ☐   Other ☐

Trade or occupation

Nature of injury

Figure 4.1 Sample accident form

E. Kind of Accident:

Contact with moving machinery ☐	Injured while lifting/carrying ☐	Trapped ☐	Exposure to explosion ☐
Struck by moving object ☐	Slip/Trip/Fall same level ☐	Drowning ☐	Contact with electricity ☐
Struck by moving vehicle ☐	Fall from height ☐	Exposure ☐	Injured by animal ☐
Struck against fixed object ☐	Distance fell ☐ metres	Exposure to fire ☐	Other ☐

F. Agent(s) Involved:

Lifting equipment ☐	Process plant ☐	Live animal ☐	Ladder scaffolding ☐
Portable hand tools ☐	Stored materials ☐	Moveable container ☐	Construction formwork ☐
Vehicle ☐	Deficient atmosphere ☐	Working surface ☐	Electricity equipment ☐
Other ☐	Pathogen infection ☐	Building mining ☐	Entertainment sports equipment ☐
Describe factors indicated ☐			Any other agent ☐

G. Account of Accident or Dangerous Occurrence:

Describe how the incident happened. In the case of an accident, state what the injured person was doing at the time:

Signature of person making report _____   Date _____

be seen as a means to an end. Obvious breaches of established procedures, however, must be dealt with in the interests of everyone concerned.

The most important part of the personnel manager's operational daily safety plan is the systematic collection of accident and dangerous occurrence data for analysis purposes. It should be remembered that many dangerous occurrences happen without getting reported. This may be due to feelings of failure by the person concerned, and threats of disciplinary action for breaches of safety codes will not encourage the reporting of such incidents. Some organisations have set up confidential telephone lines in an attempt to combat this problem and show an increase in the reporting of dangerous occurrences but admit that they may still not be aware of all such instances. Safety management, therefore, must have a structured and systematic approach towards the gathering of dangerous occurrence data. While the confidential telephone idea is a sound approach to the problem it should not be relied upon as the only method of gathering information. Confidential information forms can also be used and these can be structured in such a way as to collect contributory factors required in the subsequent analysis. An example of a sample form is given in Figure 4.1. At the same time, the safety manager should have sufficient standing within the organisational structure to be able to interview any member of staff involved in a dangerous occurrence in total confidence. This method is also an important way of obtaining data. It is very likely that an employee involved in such an incident may feel worried by it. He or she may even feel fright or shock. When a dangerous occurrence takes place it is usually regarded as a good learning vehicle, but the practice must not be encouraged! Remember also that if a lesson has been learned by both employee and employer what need is there for further disciplinary action?

Having given thought to the primary data obtained for decision-making purposes, these should be supplemented wherever possible with other data published by government departments including the HSE, the Department of Social Security, the Government Statistical Office and RoSPA. The HSE in the UK publishes accident and disease data annually, but does not publish those contributory factors evident in each accident, disease or dangerous occurrence. In fact, the current official data collection Form F2508 does not request such factors contributing to these incidents. It will be necessary, therefore, to collect these locally if the safety mix is to be correctly planned, implemented, monitored and evaluated efficiently and effectively. To provide for the simple evaluation of data collected, it should be entered in a standardised form. Bearing in mind that the results may be computerised, thought needs to be given to the coding of the results. To facilitate this, the data collection process should be divided into the following broad headings:

- accident details;
- casualty information;
- details of attendant circumstances.

For administrative purposes, provision will need to be made for the identification of accidents individually and for general recording purposes. Data required by the enforcement agencies needs to form a part of this process.

Accident details

In general terms, this section must describe what happened, when the incident occurred and where the location of the accident site was. Within this section it is important that details of all equipment involved at the time of the accident are also recorded. At the same time, accident damage is noted both to equipment and surrounding environment, together with details of independent witnesses. It is also important at this stage to note any procedures adopted and whether appropriate safety precautions were taken and issued safety clothing was worn. Whether procedures were carried out or clothing worn or not is not at issue here. Questions relating to why certain factors exist are dealt with under attendant circumstances and are deemed to be contributory to the accident or occurrence.

Casualty information

Here it is necessary to record details of who was involved in the incident and the level and type of injuries received. Generally, it is thought necessary to record casualties as either killed or injured. Few accident investigators support the classification of injury types at this level. In an accident a person is either killed or injured while a non-injury may be deemed a dangerous occurrence. It is difficult to identify those separate factors which contribute to a serious injury rather than a minor injury, or what makes an incident minor rather than serious. For example, in two identical instances two people fall 20 feet from a roof. One lands on his head and is seriously injured while the other lands on his feet and suffers minor lacerations. In this case, one employee was off work for two months while the other returned to work the following day.

Where scientific research is involved there are accident injury scales for the classification of disease and injuries. It is argued that for the operational management of effective safety procedures and practices, these are unnecessary. It must be remembered that the aim of the exercise is to identify contributory factors present when an accident occurs. The sole purpose is to identify these and take remedial action. The fact that an employee was injured to varying degrees does not significantly contribute to this part of the exercise, so personnel managers need only classify injuries simply at this stage.

Attendant circumstances

This part of the procedure considers those factors which have contributed to the accident or dangerous occurrence. It will include details of the accident site and its immediate surrounds and will cater for factors which led up to and immediately preceded the accident or occurrence. Where a non-injury incident is involved it may only be necessary for a self-certification exercise to be carried out by the person involved. It is recommended that in these circumstances, the casualty detail part of the form, be suitably modified to ensure anonymity.

Care should be taken that all questions that may be regarded as subjective are completed with care. For example, if an accident occurs outside then it might be necessary to define the meaning of 'high wind', 'rain/drizzle', 'mist/fog' etc in any instructions or in training given. Indoor accidents can suffer similar difficulties of interpretation if adequate care is not exercised. For example, the difference between bright light, light and darkness will need defining as would matters referring to ventilation such as airy, breezy, windy, gusting etc.

In a recent case during a warm sunny spell, the workforce opened windows and doors to let in a cool breeze. The breeze was rather strong and blew over several items of equipment stored in the work area. These fell over and one injured a worker's foot, while another had dust blown into her eyes thus causing the worker to catch her fingers in a machine. Here, the contributory factors were identified as the weather, the open windows and doors, the windy, blustery conditions, the loose materials capable of being blown over and the dust in the room. The casualty rate could have been affected by the removal of any one (or more) of these factors. Similarly, a person slipped and fell in a car park, because rain which fell for the first time in eight weeks mixed with oil and rubber, and caused the car park surface to become very slippery. The employee, hurrying into the office to avoid getting wet, slipped and broke a leg.

Where people fail to cope with their environment, most data collected for accident analysis purposes can be standardised. There can, of course, be allowances made for the occasional variations which exist between different occupations and industries.

Sources of data

Good accident investigation techniques require an effective database from which to work. It is necessary systematically to obtain information relating to accidents which will enable the personnel manager to identify contributory factors. One recognised form of gathering information is by using a survey.

The purpose of surveys is to obtain information about accidents. Obtaining this information can be expensive in terms of time and money. Before collecting any sort of data, thought must be given to how relevant it is to the needs of the situation, how it can be analysed usefully and how it can be obtained. The following is a brief description of a very complex subject and further reading references are given at the end of the chapter.

Factors which undoubtedly need consideration when choosing the various sources of data are:

- the value of the data;
- the ability to cross check key information;
- time taken to collect;
- cost of collection;
- accessibility (particularly internal records);
- political sensitivity.

Cost/benefit aspects should also be considered in making the choice. Clearly, subjective judgement will play an important role in this choice as the implication of various data decisions may be unclear.

There is also a great need to assess the ability to analyse data prior to collecting it. It is not uncommon to discover, after great effort and expenditure of time, the following:

- that there is too much data for manual analysis;
- that the form of the data collected is not united with the form of analysis to be applied.

Sources of primary and secondary information

The establishment of a sound and credible information base is essential for any project evaluation. Common failings in many project and

---

research investigations include:

- a failure to identify potential sources (ie insufficient initial research);
- a failure to use sources (being deterred by effort, time, cost or political antagonism);
- poor choice of sources (using subjective data when objective data is possible; failing to build in validation processes; failing to identify the sensitivity of the end decision to data accuracy).

A simple classification of data sources could be by the following means.

1. Primary data This is the information which originates from your investigation about:

- what people/systems do (observation and experimentation);
- what people say (questioning and expert opinion).

2. Secondary data This information does not originate from the investigation and covers:

- what people have done/said (internal records);
- past performance of systems (external published sources).

Primary data

Gathering data for specific needs often forces greater thought about what you are trying to do and what contribution will the piece of data make?

Gathering data in this way often provides the opportunity for personal contact, obtaining specific pieces of feedback or just developing thought in order to provide a greater insight into the nature of the problem. Almost without exception, some cross-checks will be needed of secondary data by means of primary data and vice versa.

OBSERVATION

These methods use some kind of recorder, either human or mechanical (eg video cameras, or the human eye etc). It is the aim of such methods to avoid any abnormal behaviour of the system due to the observation and is far from easy. Examples of such an approach include:

- activity sampling surveys (working on a new piece of equipment to record what happens);
- filming a specific activity in a department;
- traffic-flow counters;

- visual checks on floor utilisation;
- safety studies.

EXPERIMENTATION

The aim is to identify the difference in the outputs of a changed system with those prior to or in, an unchanged situation. The content of the use is in the testing out of a cause/effect model which has resulted from assessment of the current situation. Examples could be:

- testing new equipment;
- testing new procedures;
- testing safety ideas.

Questioning

This is the most common source of primary data and involves the use of interviews and/or questionnaires. Asking questions is a good method of establishing and cross-checking causal models and is the only way to get at behavioural problems in an organisation. Considerable skill in the use of interviews and questioning techniques is required if data is to be obtained which is worth analysing as a basis for useful information. The ease with which this source can be misleading or inaccurate is evidenced by the disastrous results of schemes based almost entirely upon data from such sources. The cost and time attached to the use of this source is influenced by the geographic dispersion of the people involved, the number of people involved and the technique chosen. These issues will be discussed below.

EXPERT OPINION

There are certain situations where the processing of data is best supplemented by the evidence of an expert. For example:

- evidence from a scientist specialising in a particular field relevant to the study;
- production controller estimating delivery of new equipment;
- union representative on reactions of his or her members to a new procedure.

The reasons for including expert opinion fall into the following three categories:

- when the rules for processing the data to form information are not available outside the mind of the individual;
- the data cannot fully be established as they are in the subconscious as well as the conscious mind;

- the worth of extracting the data etc, is not offset by the benefits of greater accuracy (often a general indication is all that would be required).

Secondary data

Such data tends to be easily accessible and is often a good starting point for an investigation. Desk work based upon such data can be helpful in the following areas:

- defining terms, gaining understanding in new fields of knowledge;
- widening viewpoints on relevant issues;
- establishing the current 'state of the art' in specific areas;
- identifying the areas where primary data will contribute;
- formulating possible approaches to resolving the problem;
- obtaining some understanding of the environment under investigation;
- providing a theoretical background to the study.

INTERNAL RECORDS

Most organisations keep many internal records, some formally, some informally, and these records can be of great value once project work is located and released. Skills in interviewing and gaining personal acceptance are often a pre-requisite to this. As a base internal records can reveal accounts, costings, labour and some accident statistics.

EXTERNAL PUBLISHED DATA

A large volume of up-to-date, published data is accessible which can be obtained from professional organisations, trade associations, libraries and colleges of higher education, usually within 14 days.

Since most problem situations are by no means unique, it is highly likely that there will be some comment in the published literature relevant to the problem being investigated. Even so, the use of such external published data is underestimated. It is important when using external data sources that the context of any findings is assessed for its real validity prior to local use.

Comparative studies

The result of collecting primary and secondary data will provide a base for formulating a hypothesis about future behaviour of systems or people which will be significant in the recommendations of any change. The use of comparison and analogy can often give further insight and affect the confidence in a model. The usefulness of this method lies in the suitability of the comparison chosen.

Comparative studies can offer the following:

- a cross-check on how to solve a problem;
- An indication of similarities and differences in approach;
- identification of the results and associated side-effects to compare with predictions.

Accident data collection

Decisions will always be influenced by a person's perception of those elements of the environment, internal or external to the organisation, which are seen to be relevant. Thus, a greater understanding of issues and their relevance to a particular decision, along with a more realistic picture of the environment, will lead to a better basis for decision.

Information is often required to:

- clarify the request of the client;
- identify issues relevant to the problem or the decision;
- enable projections to be made of the future behaviour of people and systems;
- establish the current situation and what has led up to it;
- formulate an approach to resolving the problem;
- check personal ideas against those of others.

There are eight steps involved in establishing a data or information base. These are:

- an identification of the data requirements;
- an identification of potential sources of data;
- a selection of sources to be used;
- a selection of the method to be used for collecting data;
- planning the method of data collection and the analysis which will follow;
- collecting the data;
- analysing the data;
- presenting the information in a clear and understandable form.

Data often exists in a form which has little value as an aid to specific decision making. In converting data into a meaningful form of information, one or more of the following should be considered:

- aggregation or disaggregation of the data;
- regrouping and/or ordering of the data;

- testing relationships between various types of data;
- trying various methods of presenting the data.

It is often only by trying different approaches to, and combinations, of the above, that insight and ultimate understanding can be achieved.

What is data

Data is often thought to be numerical and to consist only of such things as sets of numbers, graphs, equations and the like. On reflection, it is clear that this cannot be so since many decisions in our daily life are made on the basis of non-numeric information. Data can be anything which describes the attributes of a situation, system, person, object etc. For example, if we wished to describe the safety department in which we work, it could be done in a variety of ways:

- by number of staff;
- by sex of staff;
- by age of staff;
- by attitudes;
- by hobbies;
- by task undertaken.
- by length of service.

There is almost an infinite amount of data concerned with such a department: some of this data is objective (such as numbers, sex, age etc); while some of the data is subjective (such as attitudes etc).

The boundary between objective and subjective is often imprecise and is dependent upon the particular characteristic chosen and the form of measurement used. How could the safety procedures in your organisation be classified?

Equally, some data are quantitative (ie measurable, countable), for example numbers, while some data sets are qualitative (ie rankable, assignable), for example hobbies and rigorous mathematical methods of analysis are available for dealing with both types of data.

Accident data collection

A specific example used by some organisations to gather data is Stats Form 1 which is shown in Figure 4.2. This serves to show the level and type of information which could be gathered, which is also sympathetic to Form F2508 as required by the HSE. Such a form may need modification depending upon the industry in which it is to be used. The important thing to remember is that contributory factors need to be identified and any form design should attempt to identify these. The form shown in Figure 4.2 would need an accompanying sheet explaining each question.

The first part of the form should give the employer a reference numbering sequence that will identify each individual accident record, but also keep a tally on accident numbers per year. It must be remembered that one accident can produce more than one casualty so care must be exercised when carrying out accident analysis as opposed to casualty analysis.

A note must be kept of the accident location and this can be made simpler by using factory, building and room numbers for computing purposes. Individual workstations can also be numbered. Locations showing a high accident rate should be investigated separately. It is useful to record accident costs and there are many methods used to calculate these (see Chapter 6). It is important to keep a record of accident severity and again it is only necessary to distinguish between fatal, injury and non-injury type accidents.

In terms of the accident details then, it is important to record the date, time and exact location of the accident clearly. For road accidents, it will be necessary to use the standard grid reference conventions. Numbers killed and injured should be recorded and whether the accident occurred inside or outside. It will be necessary to list activities carried out by an employee whilst carrying out his/her duties. These should then be classified numerically for computer purposes. Activities or manoeuvres would vary with each industry, so careful planning is required. For example, a scaffolder may have an activity chart as follows:

00 Loading scaffolding from depot into vehicle
01 Securing load to vehicle
02 Travelling to/from site
03 Road traffic accident
04 Vehicle accident off the public highway
05 Unloading materials on site
06 Erecting scaffolding on site (ground level)
07 Erecting scaffolding on site (above ground level < 15 metres high)
08 Erecting scaffolding on site (above ground level > 15 metres high)
09 Carrying out safety checks on completion
10 Climbing up
11 Climbing down
12 Dismantling scaffolding
13 Removing scaffolding from site (ground level)
14 Using tools during assembly/dismantling
15 Other (please specify)

Accident types may follow the conventions used by the HSE and

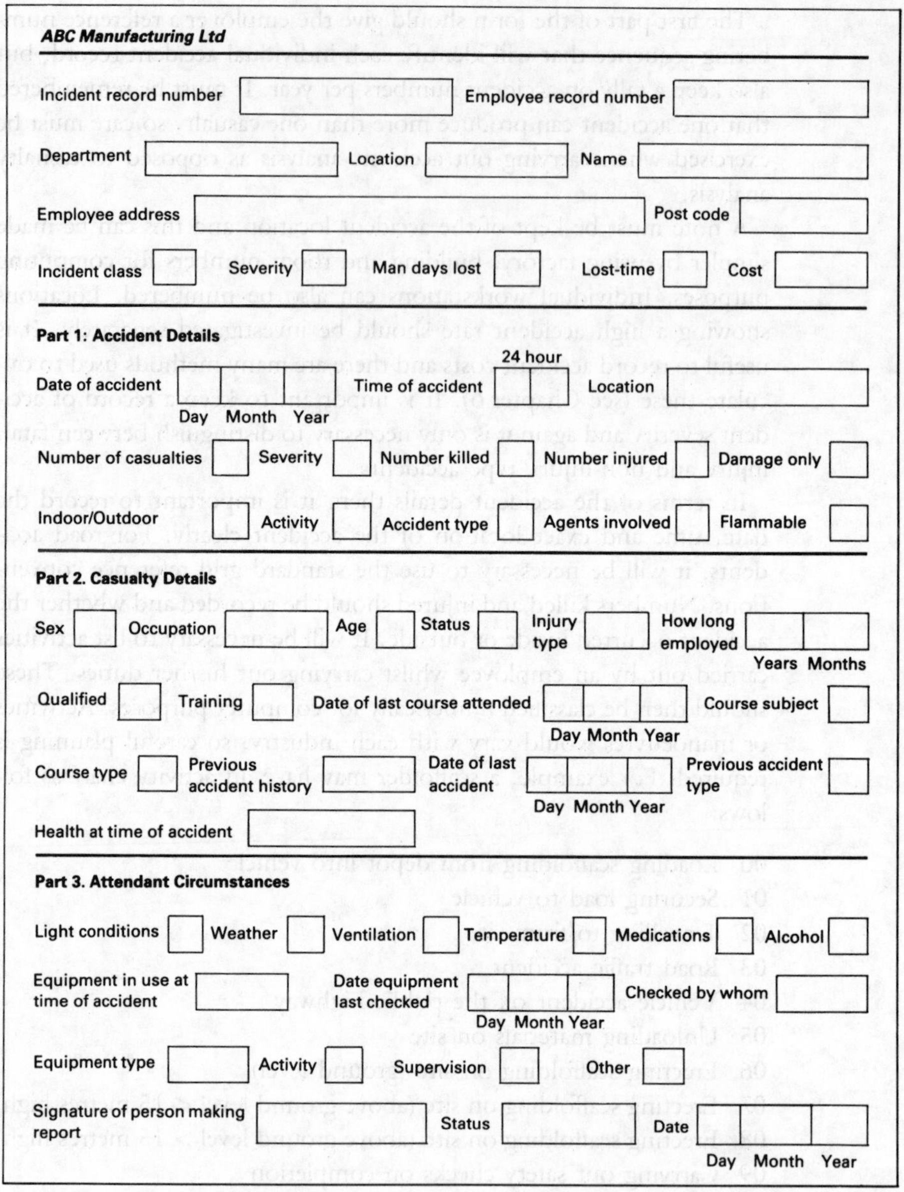

ABC Manufacturing Ltd

Incident record number | Employee record number

Department | Location | Name

Employee address | Post code

Incident class | Severity | Man days lost | Lost-time | Cost

Part 1: Accident Details

Date of accident (Day Month Year) | Time of accident (24 hour) | Location

Number of casualties | Severity | Number killed | Number injured | Damage only

Indoor/Outdoor | Activity | Accident type | Agents involved | Flammable

Part 2. Casualty Details

Sex | Occupation | Age | Status | Injury type | How long employed (Years Months)

Qualified | Training | Date of last course attended (Day Month Year) | Course subject

Course type | Previous accident history | Date of last accident (Day Month Year) | Previous accident type

Health at time of accident

Part 3. Attendant Circumstances

Light conditions | Weather | Ventilation | Temperature | Medications | Alcohol

Equipment in use at time of accident | Date equipment last checked (Day Month Year) | Checked by whom

Equipment type | Activity | Supervision | Other

Signature of person making report | Status | Date (Day Month Year)

Figure 4.2 Accident and dangerous occurrence reporting form

outlined in Section E of their Form F2508, as would agents involved in matters referring to flammable items.

Casualty details should be straightforward and should provide information concerning the person injured or involved in the dangerous occurrence. Base data should also include questions relating to the experience and professional competence of the casualty and their ability to carry out their tasks adequately and in safety. Injury type classification should be simple and might follow the following format:

01 Head
02 Neck
03 Shoulder (left)
04 Shoulder (right)
05 Chest
06 Arm (left)
07 Arm (right)
08 Wrist (left)

09 Wrist (right)
10 Hand (left)
11 Hand (right)
12 Waist
13 Hips
14 Leg (left)
15 Leg (right)
16 Ankle (left)
17 Ankle (right)
18 Foot (left)
19 Foot (right)

Further codes could be added to identify cuts, fractures, bruising etc. It may be appropriate to seek medical advice prior to setting up individual injury type codes.

Information concerning a casualty's previous accident involvement is an important consideration, as are details of training courses undertaken. Course titles should be listed in a similar manner as those listed above under 'activity'. It has been found necessary by some industries to ascertain an employee's health at the time of the accident and some organisations are able to carry out their own medical examinations periodically. In these cases it is usual to include on the form the date the last company medical examination took place.

The section on attendant circumstances in the Stats form in Figure 4.2 lists 'light conditions' as its first question. In some industries adequate lighting is important, particularly for outdoor activities such as building sites, or in the clothing industry where sewing machines are in use. In an outdoor situation, it might be appropriate to list light conditions as follows:

01 Cloudy
02 Clear and sunny
03 Dull and overcast
04 Bright
05 Hazy
06 Foggy visibility < 50 metres
07 Foggy visibility > 50 metres
08 Artificial light – streetlighting (all working)
09 Artificial light – streetlighting (not all working)
10 Artificial light – spotlighting (all working)
11 Artificial light – spotlighting (not all working)
12 Artificial light – sodium/security lighting (all working)
13 Artificial light – sodium/security (not all working)

14 Artificial lighting inadequate

15 Other (please specify)

Internal lighting and ventilation can similarly be broken down. With regard to temperature, internal temperatures should conform to the criteria listed in the Factories Act 1961. For both internal and outside temperatures, the actual temperature as recorded by a thermometer should be used. Weather conditions may be recorded as follows:

01 Dry (no wind)

02 Dry and windy (Beaufort scales 1 to 12)

03 Wet but not raining

04 Raining

05 Fine rain or drizzle

06 Icy (confirmed by temperature reading)

07 Snow (but not snowing)

08 Snowing (no wind)

09 Snowing (with wind) causing drifting

Where medications are prescribed to an employee it must be ascertained whether these might affect their performance. Medical advice should be sought in cases where a casualty has been taking medication thought to have contributed to the accident. Similarly, the consumption of alcohol should be monitored. Evidence suggests that alcohol in the workplace is becoming a problem and the only way to discover its involvement in accidents is to seek this information at the outset.

Equipment in use at the time the accident occurred should be itemised together with information concerning the correct use of protective and/or safety clothing. Information regarding equipment/safety clothing maintenance is also important and should be recorded with details of the person responsible for carrying out these checks.

One would need to list (similar to an inventory) all those items of equipment used by employees. These must be coded in a way suitable for computerisation. Within this section it is important to identify whether safety/protective clothing or other measures were used in accordance with laid-down instructions. For the agricultural industry the list might be as follows:

01 Chain-saw used in accordance with laid-down procedure and full safety equipment worn or used

02 Chain-saw not used in accordance with laid-down procedure but full safety equipment worn or used

03 Chain-saw used in accordance with laid-down procedure but full safety equipment not worn or used

04   Chain-saw not used in accordance with laid-down procedure and full safety equipment not worn or used

In some cases, certain items of equipment not deemed to be potentially hazardous may be omitted from the listing until such time as they may be involved in an accident. For example, at a school, a pencil was not regarded as hazardous until one injured a pupil. In this case the pupil had just gone to the front of the class to sharpen his pencil in a desk-mounted drum-type sharpener. He had obtained permission from the teacher in charge to do this. On returning to his desk, the pupil tripped over the strap of a school bag and fell forward over a desk on to another pupil, stabbing the pupil in the arm with the recently sharpened pencil and requiring the injured pupil to undergo hospital treatment. Up until this point, pencils had not been a feature of the equipment heading within the computerised data collection process. Since they have been added the local authority concerned have experienced several pencil-type accidents, both in and out of school premises. Remedial action has resulted in the removal of the barrel-type pencil sharpeners and the teachers now give small, hand-held sharpeners to pupils while in their seats. This action has significantly reduced pencil-related accidents.

Over a period of time comparisons with the equipment inventory can show those individual items of equipment which feature in accidents against those that do not. This is a satisfactory way of establishing which items are dangerous and allows the safety practitioner to build his or her equipment records on a regular basis.

Having identified the equipment it is necessary to identify in some way the activity being undertaken at the time of the accident. If we take the example of the chain-saw, the activity codings could look like this:

01   Tree surgery (above ground level) using safety harness
02   Tree surgery (ground level)
03   Tree surgery (above ground level using ladders)
04   Cutting tree into logs
05   Hedge/bush pruning
06   Hedge/bush removal
07   Cutting other wood types
08   Other (please specify)

It is important to record casualty supervision details. All too often supervisors and managers overlook their responsibilities to supervise subordinates when carrying out their duties. Recent examples included the Clapham rail accident and the Zeebrugge ferry disaster, where there was evidence that subordinates were unsupervised. At Clapham a signal repair engineer was said to have left certain aspects of his work in an unsafe condition. His supervisor or line manager failed to notice this omission. Likewise on the Zeebrugge ferry it was claimed that the junior member of staff responsible for closing the bow doors was asleep. His supervisor or line manager failed to notice this and to take appropriate action. With leadership comes responsibility. This cannot be ignored when things go wrong and those who absolve themselves of this duty show extremely poor management practice. This is particularly noticeable when management blame subordinates, or allow subordinates to take the blame, for not doing their jobs correctly. The process of responsibility carries upward until it can proceed no further.

It is useful to include on any data collection form a means for obtaining 'other' information which may be regarded as 'special projects'. This can facilitate the recording of information without necessarily requiring a new print run. Although only one box is provided in our example, some organisations include as many as six 'special project' or 'other' boxes at any one time.

Gathering information from people

Gathering information from people concerns two common methods of collecting primary data: the interview and the questionnaire. There are other methods available such as experimentation, observation, self-recording and so on, but these are relatively sophisticated and rarely applicable to operational project conditions.

The choice

The basic decision whether to use the questionnaire or interview is almost always concerned with resources and the scope of the problem.

- How much time and effort and manpower can be allocated to the project?
- Where are the sources of data located?
- What kind of data is needed?

By considering these questions, one of these methods can often be rejected, so easing the decision to be made. In more marginal situations, the choice can only be made by making a direct comparison of the two methods.

The questionnaire

Advantages:

- it can be administered to groups of people at the same time, thus saving time and expense;
- it can be used where the respondents are spread over a wide geographical area;
- the required answers on a questionnaire can be pre-structured thus making the task of analysis much easier;
- questionnaires can be more reliable than interviews;
- questionnaires can be made anonymous, allowing for more freedom of response;
- questionnaires give the respondent the opportunity to verify factual data;
- questionnaires avoid interviewer 'error'.

Disadvantages:

- questionnaires often obtain a low response rate, giving rise to problems of representativeness;
- respondents can also avoid answering specific questions;
- difficult questions cannot be clarified by the respondent;
- questionnaires are often seen to be impersonal and respondents do not feel committed to filling them in;
- there is no opportunity to ask extra questions on a questionnaire so new data is missed.

Conducting formal interviews

It is important to deal with some of the general principles of the interview before specific safety examples are discussed. The interview is a face-to-face verbal exchange, in which one person, the interviewer, attempts to elicit information or expressions of opinion, attitudes or belief from another person or persons.

The role of the interview is to act as a method for collecting data and may be used:

- during the early stages of an investigation to help identify the problem areas, the relevant dimensions, to suggest hypotheses and to reveal the natural frames of reference existing in the minds of the respondents;
- if questionnaires are to be used, the interview may be employed to pre-test the questionnaire form;
- as the main instrument of data collection;
- to clarify findings which have emerged from other sources of data.

Advantages:

- interviews increase respondents' commitment;
- they tend to be more valid, encouraging true-to-life answers;
- interviews often bring to the surface data which would not come out in a questionnaire;
- they allow for clarification of difficult questions.

Disadvantages:

- problems of interviewer error, taking account of appearance, manner and style of asking questions;
- problems of anonymity or the lack of it;
- unstructured interviews often provide data in a form which is difficult to analyse;
- interviews are time-consuming.

The structured versus the unstructured interview

A standardised interview is one in which the questions have been decided upon in advance of the interview. The questions are asked with the same wording and in the same order for each respondent. The essential feature of a structured interview is that the interviewer does not have the freedom to re-word questions, to introduce questions which seem especially applicable to the individual case, or to change the order of topics to conform to the interviewer's spontaneous sequence of ideas. In the unstructured interview, the interviewer technique is completely flexible and can vary from one respondent to the next.

Structured interviews:

- incorporate a basic principle of measurement (that of making information comparable from case to case);
- are more reliable;
- minimise errors due to question wording.

Unstructured interviews:

- permit standardisation of meanings, rather than the more superficial aspects of the stimulus situation (the question);
- are likely to be more valid in that they encourage more true-to-life responses;
- are more flexible.

Questions

For both interviews and questionnaires, it is necessary to relate questions to the problems under study. However, the discipline of refining questions and making sure that they are relevant can be difficult. For example, is a question pertaining to an employee's hobbies relevant to the study?

There are a few basic rules that can be applied to the framing of questions:

- avoid ambiguous words or phrases;
- avoid long questions;
- the questions should state as precisely as possible the time, place and context you want the respondent to assume;
- either make explicit all the alternatives the respondent could answer or none of them;
- avoid multiple questions;
- avoid leading questions;
- avoid rhetorical questions;
- avoid implied values.

It has been widely assumed that the interview is superior in many ways and must be used whenever resources permit. Certainly the interview should be used at the exploratory stages, particularly in the area of accident investigation. Because of the seriousness of the accident investigation process and the legal requirements to make all workplaces safer such an interview may be referred to as a statement interview or formal interview.

Statement or formal interviews

If statements are considered to be part of the operational plan then it is important that they are taken as quickly as possible after the event, normally within 24 hours of the accident happening. As early as 1932, psychologists were able to show that a person is likely to forget half of what they originally perceived after 24 hours. To take a statement after this period of time can result in memory loss which may affect important details, or other factors may influence the interviewee to distort the facts. For example a high-status questioner may influence a witness. A motorist stopped by the police would think carefully about what he or she said to the constable because of the fear of prosecution. In this case, the police officer becomes a high-status questioner. Likewise, an insurance company receives many reports each year from clients involved in road traffic accidents purporting that trees have mysteriously appeared in the path of their vehicle! In these cases, the insurance company is seen as the high-status questioner in that the client's no-claims bonuses may be affected if they are found to be blameworthy. In such examples, a distortion of the facts is common.

It should be understood that the prime objective of taking statements is to ascertain facts relating to an accident or dangerous occurrence, which will facilitate the introduction of remedial measures which are specifically designed to prevent or reduce the incidence of those events happening in the future. The taking of statements should not be seen solely as a means of apportioning blame or for deciding upon disciplinary action. The safety practitioner conducting an interview may wish to obtain these facts in total confidence. Some organisations provide confidential phone lines for the reporting of dangerous occurrences. This practice can be recommended.

Disciplinary action must always be used wisely and should only be considered after all the evidence has been presented. It is more important that the interview is taken and conducted in a professional manner. These issues are discussed below.

Conduct of the formal interview

It is unwise to allow an employee to make a statement concerning an accident without supervision. To do so may mean that vital contributory factors are omitted from the report. It is more appropriate to conduct an interview which is constructed in such a manner as to provide a basis for the systematic gathering of relevant factors pertaining to the accident or occurrence. It is important that these interviews are seen primarily as fact-finding exercises.

It has been said that there is a wealth of evidence which questions witness reliability but the reliability of the victim statement can also be questioned, particularly when the consequences of the accident are understood and possible disciplinary or other punitive action could result. Here the interview technique should be used for fact finding only so that the investigator can learn more about the contributory factors which came together to cause the accident.

Geiselman and Fisher (1986), describe three types of interview techniques. These are the cognitive, hypnosis and interrogative-type interview. Here, hypnosis means what it says and the interrogative type interview is the type which might be expected from the police. The most effective methods were found to be the cognitive and hypnosis methods. The latter was rejected for practical terms due to the length of training necessary to hypnotise people. The ethics of hypnotism are also questionable. The cognitive-type interview was found to be equally as good and easier to learn. Basically, this method consists of four general points for jogging memory, plus several specific techniques which are outlined below. The safety manager should consider these points in order to help them to obtain more reliable information from injured members of the workforce. The four points should be explained to the interviewee before the narrative report. The first two attempt to increase the overlap of elements between the stored memory and the retrieval mechanisms. The last two encourage the use of several retrieval paths. They are as follows.

1. Reconstruct the circumstances Here the interviewer asks the witness or victim to reconstruct the incident in general terms. Reconstruct the circumstances that surrounded the incident. Get the interviewee to:

- think about the environment in which the accident happened, such as room layout, furniture locations, weather, vehicles, equipment, lighting and other people or objects;
- think about what they were doing before the accident happened, how they were feeling and their reactions to the incident.

It is important to start before the accident happened and it may be necessary to start 24 hours before the accident happened as evidence exists to show that stress at home, alcohol and other factors can feature as major contributory factors in an accident happening.

2. Report everything The investigator should explain that all information may be helpful and nothing should be omitted, even if is thought to be irrelevant. All information should be given. Some people tend to think that some information is not important so they hold back. Do not ask your casualty or witness to edit anything.

3. Recall events in a different order It is natural to ask the person being interviewed to start at the beginning and journey through to the end. If you have done this, it is worth asking for the information in reverse order or to try starting with the point that concerned the interviewee the most about the event. From here you may go forward or backwards in time.

4. Change perspectives Try to see the event from another person's point of view or adopt the perspectives of others who were present at the scene.

Mental reconstruction of circumstances surrounding a memorable event has been shown to be a powerful aid to memory and a visit to the accident-site and undertaking accident reconstruction exercises are valuable.

In addition to the four points outlined above, the cognitive interview also uses a series of specific questions to help an accident investigator elicit information following the narrative phase of an interview. The investigator might consider asking the following.

- Was the casualty qualified to carry out the task being undertaken at the time of the accident?
- Was safety clothing worn?
- When did the casualty last undertake relevant safety training?
- When was equipment involved in the accident last examined?
- Were safety procedures followed?
- Was the casualty fit to undertake his or her duties?
- Have the contributory factors been identified?
- How could these have been eliminated at the time and how can they be eliminated for the future?

These questions are of a general nature and should not be regarded as exhaustive. They are given as a general indication of the type of information which must come out of an interview situation when accidents have occurred. The aim of the exercise must be accident prevention in the future, and a decision will have to be taken as to the safety mix required. Enforcement on its own is ineffective so taking disciplinary action alone cannot be recommended. It must be used in conjunction with other measures which must be elicited from the investigation.

┌─ *CHECKLIST* ───┐

- do you understand the importance of accident investigation as a tool for accident reduction programme planning?
- do you have an adequate accident investigation procedure?
- are your data collection and analysis procedures adequate?
- do you have an effective means of collecting dangerous occurrence information?
- have you a procedure for interviewing witnesses for all levels and type of accident and/or dangerous occurrence?
- do you interview accident casualties with the sole purpose of identifying contributory factors to the incident?
- are the procedures for storing this information appropriate and adequate for the purpose?

└──┘

CHAPTER 5
Occupational Hygiene and Health

This chapter is divided into two Parts. In Part 1 we shall be looking at fire procedures, first-aid, heating, lighting, ventilation, noise and vibration, and radiation with regard to VDUs. Part 1 finishes with a look at protective clothing, manual handling and dangerous substances. In Part 2 we examine the areas of welfare, alcohol and drugs, stress management, cleaning and hygiene.

PART 1

Fire procedures

In this paragraph we will consider the following:

- fire precautions legislation;
- fire appliances and equipment;
- fire signing and escapes;
- fire certificates;
- fire insurance;
- fire prevention;
- fire procedures.

Fire precautions and legislation

The relevant law concerning fire precautions is to be found in the following:

Fire Precautions Act 1971 (and regulations and orders made thereunder)
Fire Safety and Safety of Places of Sport Act 1987
Health and Safety at Work Act 1974
Building Act 1984
Building Regulations 1985
Fire Service Act 1947

The prime piece of legislation is the Fire Precautions Act 1971 which was amended by the Fire Safety and Safety of Places of Sport Act 1987. This act applies to all premises in use irrespective of whether they are industrial, commercial or public. The local fire authority is empowered to enforce these requirements under duties and powers specified in the Fire Services Act 1947. Generally, all fire provisions in industry and commerce in respect of fire escapes, alarms and the like are the responsibility of the fire authority but premises containing hazardous or flammable materials and/or explosives are controlled by the HSE. Section 2 of the Health and Safety at Work Act 1974 provides for measures to be undertaken by employers in respect of fire extinguishers, fire training and drills.

Fire appliances and equipment

There are basically five types of fire extinguisher:

- water extinguishers which are coloured red;
- foam extinguishers which are coloured cream;
- dry powder extinguishers which are coloured blue;
- carbon dioxide extinguishers which are coloured black;
- vaporising extinguishers which are coloured green.

Table 5.1 shows the application of each type of extinguisher.

A manually operated fire alarm is required in all premises holding a fire certificate (see below). Such a system must comply with the current

Table 5.1 *Fire appliances and equipment checklist*

Class of fire	Description	Extinguisher type
A	Solid materials usually organic with glowing embers	Water, foam, dry powder, vaporising liquid or CO_2
B	Liquids and liquifiable solids such as:	Water, foam (ensure stability in miscible solvents), dry powder and CO_2
	miscible with water, acetone or methanol	
	immiscible with water such as petrol benzene, waxes and fats	Foam, dry powder CO_2 or vaporising liquid

Class of extinguisher	Colour	Quantity	Location	Date last checked
Water	Red			
Foam	Cream			
Carbon dioxide				
(CO_2)	Black			
Dry powder	Blue			
Vaporising liquid	Green			

Code of Practice for the installation of fire alarms and appropriate fire equipment must be used. Such a system should be tested every three months and the results recorded. Emergency lighting may also be required.

It may be necessary to provide fire wardens (see *Fire procedures*, below) with a torch and an armband so that they are easily recognisable during a building evacuation.

Kitchens areas should also be provided with a fire blanket.

Fire signing

It is important that all escape routes are adequately signed and that such signing is kept clear and can easily be seen. Damaged or old, dirty signs should be replaced regularly. All escape routes must be kept clear and unobstructed, and should allow the quick and easy evacuation of a room or building. All means of escape should provide the following:

- all doors affording a means of escape, though not in continuous use, should be clearly indicated;
- sliding doors should clearly show the direction in which they open;
- doors affording a means of escape should be regularly maintained;
- doors affording escape should not be obstructed or locked.

No smoking areas should be clearly identified and staff made aware of such rules and regulations. Combustible waste should be kept away from smoking areas and in metal containers with appropriately tight-fitting lids.

Smoking should only be permitted in well-ventilated areas away from combustible or flammable liquids and materials. Ashtrays must be provided with a sand or water base and must be used.

Where a building has several floors serviced by a lift then each floor should be clearly marked so that visitors or new employees can readily identify where they are and follow the appropriate fire exit signs. Stairways should be similarly marked.

Fire certificates

These are issued by:

- local fire authorities; or
- the HSE.

It should be noted that the situations requiring compulsory certification under the Fire Precautions Act 1971 have been deregulated under the Fire Safety and Safety of Places of Sport Act 1987. A certificate may now be required in the following circumstances:

- buildings containing two or more factory and/or office premises where the number of persons employed in all of them at any one time is in excess of 20 people;
- buildings containing two or more office and/or factory premises where the number of persons employed at any one time in all of them other than on the ground floor exceeds 10 persons;
- factories where explosives or highly flammable materials are stored or used in or around the premises, unless in the opinion of the fire authority there is no serious risk to persons in the vicinity.

A fire authority may grant an exemption from the certification requirements of the Fire Precautions Act 1971 as amended under the Fire Safety and Safety of Places of Sport Act 1987. Personnel managers in doubt as to their particular requirements should contact their local fire prevention officer for further advice.

Fire insurance

The general requirements applying to insurance are covered in Chapter 3. However, there are some specific points to consider which apply specifically to fire insurance. It is usual only for direct loss caused by fire to be insured. It should be noted that damage to property caused by falling debris will be insured if destroyed by fire, but damage caused by subsequent explosion would not. It is important that all insurance policies are reviewed annually to ensure that adequate cover is provided. If in doubt contact your insurance broker.

Fire prevention

Good housekeeping, safe storage of flammable materials and appropriate no smoking rules are usually cheap and simple ways of reducing the risk of fires. For organisations using or storing highly flammable or explosive materials, they must provide storage areas designed especially for this purpose. Personnel managers who may have any doubts as to their duties and responsibilities in this respect should seek professional advice regarding the appropriate steps to be taken. The local health and safety inspectorate or local fire authority will assist in such cases. Their advice is usually free of charge.

Fire training is an important aspect of fire prevention and it is important that key personnel are familiar with basic fire fighting techniques. Action which is taken quickly and correctly can prevent a fire spreading. There are three fundamental aspects to extinguishing a fire. These are:

- **starvation** this can be achieved by removing the fuel from the fire, isolating the fire from the fuel source or reducing the bulk of the fuel source present;
- **smothering** by removing the supply of oxygen in covering the fire with a fire blanket or an inert gas;
- **cooling** by dowsing the fire and fuel with water.

Table 5.2 illustrates the types of fire and the correct extinguishers to be used. It should be remembered that the fire brigade should be called whenever a fire is detected however small you think it might be.

Fire procedures

It is important that fire procedures are communicated to all staff regularly. Such procedures should be tested at regular intervals in order to evaluate their effectiveness. Each department or floor should have a fire warden appointed who is responsible for ensuring that all persons are evacuated safely in the event of a fire or fire drill. Such a person should be in possession of a torch and a record of everyone working in the area

Table 5.2 *Types of fire extinguisher to be used*

Type of extinguisher	Colour	Fire type
Water	Red	Suitable for ordinary fires involving wood or paper but not flammable liquids. Not to be used for fires involving electricity.
Foam	Cream	Suitable for small liquid fires or small oil fires where foam can be used to smother the fire. Foam may not put out a fire on a vertical plane.
Dry powder	Blue	Suitable for flammable liquids and electrical fires.
Vaporising	Green	Suitable for electrical or electronic equipment fires. May be used for flammable liquid fires but does produce toxic gases. The hotter the fire the worse are the toxic gases.
Carbon dioxide	Black	Suitable for fires involving electrical equipment.

of their responsibility. This must include visitors. To facilitate this it is necessary for all employees and visitors to sign in or out. When the alarm is sounded, all employees and visitors will proceed by the most direct route to their pre-selected assembly points. The fire warden will immediately search rest rooms, toilets and other places in order to ensure that everyone is evacuating the premises. On arrival at the assembly point a roll-call must be taken. The fire incident officer may require this information in the event of a real fire.

Personnel managers must ensure that this procedure is communicated to all staff and that it is regularly tested. Everyone must book in or out, and the location of staff must be known by the fire warden. In the event of a real fire, it is totally unacceptable to ask fire officers to enter dangerous buildings looking for missing members of staff, only to discover they were not on the premises anyway.

It is necessary to publicise all fire procedures and assembly points.

First-aid

The obligation to provide first-aid facilities comes within the general duties under the Health and Safety at Work Act 1974. This requires employers to ensure a healthy and safe working environment for their employees. Section 2(1) requires that employers will ensure, so far as is reasonably practicable (see Chapter 1), the health, safety and welfare of all their employees. This extends to the provision of appropriate first-aid facilities. The Health and Safety (First-Aid) Regulations 1981 provide for the following:

- provision of first-aid equipment and facilities;
- first-aiders;
- first-aid room where required;
- first-aid training.

First-aid equipment and facilities

An employer must provide adequate equipment and facilities to enable first-aid to be rendered to employees who are injured at work or become ill at work.

There are four criteria used to decide what provision is necessary:

- the number of employees;
- the nature of the business;
- the size of the organisation and spread of employees;
- location of the business and employees place of work;

A summary of the criteria is given in Table 5.3.

Table 5.3 *First-aid cover requirements*

First-aiders	Employees
1	50
2	150

First-aid room	Employees
1	250

Where premises are said to be hazardous such as shipbuilding, factories, warehouses and farms there should be a trained first-aider as outlined above at all times. Where a first-aider is away or off work, cover for the absence must be provided by the employer. Where an organisation employs fewer than 50 persons then an employer must still provide for first-aid cover.

First-aiders

The first-aid regulations require that an employer must provide or make available an adequate number of suitable people who have been trained in first-aid. A person is not regarded as suitable unless that person has undertaken a course of first-aid training which has:

- been approved by the HSE; or
- been provided with additional specialised training so approved.

A suitable person may be:

- a first-aider;
- an occupational first-aider;
- another person who has approved training and qualifications (eg registered nurse or medical practitioner).

A first-aider is a person who has received approved training and holds a valid first-aid certificate.

First-aid rooms

Such a facility is required where 400 or more employees are at work. It is expected that such a facility will be appropriately staffed. 'Appropriate staff' means a minimum qualification of an occupational first-aider where:

- there are establishments with special hazards;

- the place of work is a construction site with more than 250 persons at work;
- access to casualty centres is difficult.

Otherwise, a certified first-aider is necessary.

Access to a first-aid room should be available to staff at all times when at work. Such a room should be sited in an appropriate location so as to facilitate vehicular access in order that injured persons may be transported to hospital with the minimum of inconvenience to everyone, including the workforce. Such a room should:

- contain suitable first-aid equipment and facilities;
- be properly ventilated;
- be adequately heated;
- have sufficient lighting;
- be clean and tidy;
- be properly maintained;
- be large enough to house a couch;
- have suitable access and egress for a stretcher, wheelchair or carrying chair;
- indicate clearly the names and locations of the nearest first-aiders.

First-aid boxes should be the responsibility of the qualified first-aider. Do not leave first-aid boxes open and unchecked, otherwise when they come to be needed they will probably be empty!

Self-employed personnel are required to provide themselves with adequate first-aid facilities and as such should carry their own first-aid kit. Professional drivers who are either employees or self-employed should also be provided with/or provide for themselves (if self employed) an approved first-aid kit for use in their vehicle while away from their depot or works.

First-aid training

It is essential that there are sufficient qualified first-aiders available on duty at any one time so as to allow for absences. Unless an organisation has sufficient numbers to train, it would probably not be financially viable to run an in-house course. However, if such a localised demand exists, then the course content, trainers and testing facilities will need to be approved by the HSE. The smaller company should usually contact:

- the St John's Ambulance Brigade;
- the British Red Cross; or
- the Health Promotion Manager of the local Health Authority.

All of these organisations will be able to advise on appropriate approved certification first-aid courses.

Heating

The legal requirements covering the provisions in respect of temperature in places of work are found in section 3 of the Factories Act 1961 and in the Offices, Shops and Railway Premises Act 1963. Also, within the general terms of the Health and Safety at Work Act 1974, every employer is required to provide and maintain a safe and healthy working environment. This includes temperature and humidity. A thermometer must be provided and the minimum acceptable temperature in an environment where workers are expected to sit for a great proportion of their time is 16°C. This temperature must be reached and maintained within one hour from the first hour of work.

There are specific regulations and statutory obligations relating to such industries as the textile industry or where artificial humidity is produced. A general summary is provided in Table 5.4.

Lighting

Most modern buildings will meet the legal requirements regarding the provision of good adequate lighting. The requirements to provide good and adequate lighting can be found in the Factories Act 1961, the Offices, Shops and Railway Premises Act 1963 with further requirements to provide a healthy and safe working environment within the terms of the Health and Safety at Work Act 1974. If an employer fails to provide and maintain a suitable standard of lighting he or she will be in breach of section 5(1) of the Factories Act 1961. It is important that personnel managers set up a system whereby lighting (eg bulb

Table 5.4 *Some common temperature requirements*

Workplace	Temperature	Essential requirements
Office	16°C (min)	Thermometer
Factory	16°C (min)	Thermometer
Steam room	22.5°C (max)	Hygrometer
Other room where artificial humidity is produced	22.5°C (max)	Hydrometer

Table 5.5 *A standard lighting checksheet*

Type of lamp	Lumens per watt	Location	Number	Date last checked
Incandescent	10 to 18			
Tungsten halogen	22			
High pressure mercury	25 to 55			
Tabular fluorescent	30 to 80			
Mercury halide	60 to 80			
High pressure sodium	100			

(Note: Incandescent lamps are the common coiled filament lamps.)

replacement) is monitored regularly and that light bulbs provide sufficient lumens per watt where natural lighting is deficient.

The intention of this section of the book is to provide sufficient information to enable adequate monitoring of lighting. To this end Table 5.5 summarises all that the personnel manager need know for daily operational purposes.

Further advice, where necessary, should be sought from an appropriately qualified lighting engineer.

Ventilation

Section 2(1) of the Health and Safety at Work Act 1974 imposes a duty on employees to provide all workers with an adequate supply of pollution-free or uncontaminated air. Because employers must provide and maintain a safe and healthy working environment, they may be criminally liable if the workplace is not adequately ventilated- and dust or contaminant-free. Moreover, in section 2(2) of the HASAWA all employers must inform, instruct and train their staff in health and safety procedures. This means that employees must know how to use, test and maintain equipment that ensures a pure air supply and controls air pollutants such as dust and fumes. In addition, sections 4 and 63 of the Factories Act 1961 contain two separate provisions in respect of:

- air purification (section 4);
- dust and fumes (section 63).

Air purification

A circulation of fresh air is necessary to:

- ensure and maintain the adequate ventilation of places of work; and
- render harmless, as far as possible, all fumes, dust and other impurities which may be harmful to health or are generated in the course of any process carried out in the factory.

Where section 4 of the Factories Act 1961 might exclude certain areas such as boiler-houses or the provision of breathing apparatus, personnel managers should be reminded that the Health and Safety at Work Act 1974 will require an employer to take all reasonable steps to ensure the health and safety of the workforce.

Table 5.6 *Some regulations covering dust and fumes*

Some specific regulations relating to dust and fumes	Relevance	
	YES	NO
Control of Asbestos at Work Regulations 1987		
Grinding of Metals (Miscellaneous) Regulations 1925 and 1950		
Grinding of Cutlery and Edge Tools Regulations 1925 and 1950		
Blasting (Casting and Other Articles), Special Regulations 1949		
Foundries (Parting Materials) Special Regulation 1950		
Non-Ferrous Metals (Melting and Foundings) Regulations 1962		
Chemical Works Regulations 1922		
Indiarubber Regulations 1922		
Chromium Plating Regulations 1931		
Iron and Steel Foundaries Regulations 1953		
Highly Flammable Liquids and Liquified Petroleum Gases Regulations 1972		
Control of Lead at Work Regulations 1980		
Factories (Flax and Tow Spinning and Weaving) Regulations 1906		
Factories (Flax and Tow Spinning and Weaving) Regulations 1907		
Jute (Safety, Health and Welfare) Regulations 1948		
Construction (General Provisions) Regulations 1961		
Smoke Control Areas Regulations 1990		

(Continue this list and keep it up to date
Also, refer back to Figure 1.7)

Composition of pure air	
Oxygen	20.94%
Carbon dioxide	0.03%
Nitrogen and other inert gases	79.03%

Table 5.7 *Some ways of controlling airborne pollution*

Type	Hazardous substance	Source	Process	Possible effect	Possible remedial action
DUST	Silica (Clay)	Dry sweeping	Pottery	Silicosis	Dampen down
	Hardwood	Sanding	Woodwork	Nasal cancer	Respirator
	Spore	Mouldy hay	Agriculture	Farmer's lung	Ventilation
FUMES	Zine	Hot flame	Flamecutting	Fume fever	Ventilation
	Cadmium	Heat	Hard solder	Emphysemia	Respirator Extractor
GAS	Nitrogen oxides	Hot flames	Welding	Lung irritation	Ventilation
	Carbon dioxide	Engine exhaust	Garages	De-oxygenation	Respirator
	Slurry gases	Fermentation	Agriculture	Asphyxiation	Extractor
VAPOUR	Perchloroethylene	Evaporation	Dry cleaning	Liver damage	Ventilation
	isocyanate	Moulding	Plastics	Asthma	Respirator Extractor
MIST	Chromic acid	Bubbles breaking	Plating	Ulceration	Ventilation
	Non-solvent oil	Machine lubricant	Engineering	Skin cancer	Protective
	Animal infection	Meat handling	Abattoir	Brucellosis	Clothing Respirator

Control of dust and fumes

This applies where:

- any dust or fumes or other impurities which are likely to impair health or are regarded as offensive to the employee, or
- substantial quantities of dust of any kind.

are given off.

Employers must take measures to:

- protect employees against the inhalation of dust, fumes and/or other impurities;
- prevent dust from accumulating in the workplace;
- provide a free flow of clean air.

A list of specific regulations referring to dust and fumes is given in Table 5.6.

Recognised methods of controlling airborne pollution are given in Table 5.7.

Noise and vibration

There is a requirement under the Health and Safety at Work Act 1974 to provide a healthy and safe working environment. It has long been accepted that exposure to severe noise and vibration can seriously threaten a person's health. In addition, the Noise at Work Regulations 1989 require:

- employers to prevent damage to hearing; and
- designers, manufacturers, importers and suppliers to prevent damage to hearing.

Employers are deemed to include self-employed persons and an employee must co-operate with their employer's programme to prevent hearing damage. Within these regulations, every employer shall ensure that a competent person makes a noise assessment which is capable of:

- identifying which employees are exposed;
- providing information with regard to noise exposure levels;
- providing a review procedure of noise levels where necessary.

Noise assessment records should be kept so that trends may be identified over longer periods of time. A sample noise assessment form is given in Table 5.8.

Every employer must undertake a programme of measures to:

- identify noise sources;
- identify remedial measures to be taken;
- implement those remedial measures;
- ensure that action is taken;
- monitor the situation;
- reassess noise exposure levels.

Table 5.8   *A simple noise assessment form*

Location	Background noise level	Peak noise level	Date of assessment	Action taken	Person responsible

Table 5.9 *A simple noise level checklist*

Noise level	Checklist	YES	NO
>85 dB(A)	Are noisy machines or processes identified by warning signs? Does everyone in the noisy area need to work there? How long can people stay in the noisy area? Have employees been warned about the dangers of noise? Have they ear protectors? Do they wear ear protectors? Has manufacturer's information about noise levels been checked? Will changes in work methods affect noise levels? Can noise be reduced by fixing loose/vibrating pieces? Can better maintenance reduce noise levels?		

Comments:

Action taken:

Signed: Date:

Factors to consider are:

● the number of workers who would benefit by the noise reduction programme;
● the noise exposure levels involved;
● a socio-technical appraisal of noise reduction strategies;
● factors which might impede wearing of ear defenders.

In areas where noise levels require remedial action, appropriate signing must be displayed warning that ear protectors must be worn.

There is a requirement to take action if workers receive a daily personal exposure to noise at or above 85dB(A) or at a peak sound pressure at or above 140dB(A)

A checklist is provided in Table 5.9.

Radiation – VDUs

In Figure 5.10 there is a table which illustrates the various types of electromagnetic radiation and shows some of the hazards that they can cause. The most common exposure to the modern office is the low frequency radiation emitted from the computer visual display unit (VDU). Some problems connected with prolonged VDU use are:

- complaints of eye discomfort such as burning, itching and soreness;
- complaints concerning blurred vision, focusing problems and squinting;
- posture complaints such as headaches, backaches, tiredness or sleepiness.

Workers exposed to prolonged VDU use should be given regular eyesight checks and steps should be taken to check:

- lighting;
- location of VDU;
- type of workstation used;
- seating;
- contrast and brightness controls;
- length of time spent at the VDU;
- size and type of VDU used;
- appropriate screen filter used.

Workers exposed to ionising radiation may need to:

- undergo regular medical examinations;
- undergo regular dose assessments;
- appoint a specialist radiation protection adviser;
- have contingency plans to cater for radioactive spills etc;
- obtain authorization for the use, storage and disposal of radioactive waste.

Protective clothing

Statutory requirements for the provision of protective clothing are laid down by several regulations made under the Factories Act 1961. Although no specific requirement is made under the HASAWA regarding protective clothing/equipment, it does state that employers cannot charge for providing it. Not only can they not charge for it, such equipment must be readily available and accessible for immediate use. Where such equipment or clothing is provided an employer must also ensure that it is used or worn correctly.

Within the general terms at common law, the duty of care which every employer owes his or her workforce requires that he or she must protect his or her employees from the risk of reasonably foreseeable injury. Whether a hazard is regarded as reasonably foreseeable must depend upon the circumstances and whether this type of incident has been experienced before.

In Table 5.10, a summary is provided which contains the requirements for protective clothing in some well known industries and illustrates which regulations refer to each requirement.

It is important that safety equipment and clothing should conform to the appropriate safety standard and these are published by the HSE. Details are provided in the supplementary reading list at the end of this chapter. Standard personal protection items would include:

- safety eye glasses;
- footwear;
- hats;
- face shields;
- gloves;
- leggings;
- waterproofs;
- ear protection;

Table 5.10 *Example list of protection requirements*

Application	Required protection	Regulations
Workplaces where bottles and syphons are manufactured	Aprons Face guards Footware Gauntlets	Aereated Water Regulations 1921
Workplaces where asbestos is used	Breathing apparatus Head covering Overalls	Control of Asbestos at Work Regulations 1987
Workplaces where construction and works of an engineering nature are carried out	Eye protectors Helmets Gloves Clothing Belts	Construction Regulations 1961 and 1966
List those carried out by your organisation	List those items of protection you must provide	List those regulations which relate to your industry

- neck protection;
- respiratory equipment;

If you provide such items you must ensure that they are worn correctly at all times.

Manual handling

The incorrect handling of products and materials has been identified as a contributory factor in the majority of minor accidents and minor injuries in the workplace. Factors to consider are:

- weight of the load;
- shape and size of the load;
- the height of the load;
- the material the load is made of;
- the condition of the floor;
- the material in which the load is contained;
- the headroom available;
- space around the load;
- the temperature of the room in which the load is stored;
- the lighting conditions.

Many training organisations now teach kinetic handling techniques which improve balance and posture for the manual aspects of load moving.

Transport

If your organisation uses transport then make sure that someone is responsible for it. In this way vehicle maintenance, driver training and so on can be effectively delegated. It is important to ensure that:

- drivers are properly trained;
- where appropriate drivers are correctly licensed to drive the vehicle on the public highway;
- no unauthorised drivers use the vehicles;
- vehicle faults are rectified as quickly as possible;
- visitors are aware of transport rules and procedures;
- supervision is available when undertaking certain manoeuvres;
- trackways/roadways are properly maintained and unobstructed;
- pedestrians and vehicles are safely segregated;
- loading bays are away from general traffic;
- drivers are protected from falling objects or vehicle roll over.

Where vehicles have to be repaired, make sure that the repairs are carried out by a competent person and that such repairs are carried out in an area specifically set aside for the purpose.

Stacking and storing

Not only is poor stacking responsible for many injuries each year, but also for damaging the stored items themselves. Ensure that:

- items which can roll are properly chocked;
- pallets are not damaged;
- containers are serviceable;
- racks are not damaged;
- stacked pallets are vertical on a level floor without overbalancing;
- packages are stacked in brick fashion so that there are no independent columns;
- where racks are used they are fixed to the wall;
- items do not block gangways/walkways or protrude;
- ladders are used at all times for climbing racks;
- heavy stacks are not leaning against retaining walls;
- de-stacking is from the top only;
- safe loading limits of racks are not exceeded.

Lifting equipment

Where lifting equipment is used ensure that:

- test certificates for all lifting machinery are up-to-date;
- safe working loads are observed by all operators;
- annual or six-monthly examination reports are available;
- only certified lifting equipment is used;
- safe working loads are not exceeded;
- loads of doubtful weight or machine adequacy are not used;
- load centres of gravity are known;
- damaged or makeshift equipment is not used;
- chains, wires, ropes are not damaged or worn;
- appropriate padding is available to avoid damage to the load when lifted;
- loads are lifted slowly and not snatched;
- cranes have the correct counterweight, load radius indicator and/or safe load indicator;
- a responsible slinger or banksman uses a recognised signalling system;
- loads do not drop from great heights;
- access to motor rooms and service pits of hoists and lifts are correct.

TAKING CARE OF SAFETY

Dangerous Substances and the Control of Substances Hazardous to Health (COSHH)

The COSHH regulations introduce a new legal framework for the control of substances hazardous to health in all types of businesses, including factories, farms, quarries, leisure and service activities, offices and shops. The regulations require an assessment of all work which is liable to expose any employee to hazardous solids, liquids, dusts, fumes, vapours, gases or micro-organisms. Assessment means evaluating the risks to health and then deciding on the action needed to remove or reduce those risks.

The responsibility to make the assessment rests with the employer. As the employer, you could lead the assessment yourself or give the task to someone else with the authority and ability to get all the necessary information, and make correct decisions about the risks and the precautions that are needed. That person should understand the point of the various requirements of the COSHH regulations and have access to a copy of the Regulations and approved code of practice. Whoever does the assessment, make sure that managers, supervisors and employees' safety representatives are fully consulted about the work processes, about what workers are doing (or are liable to be doing), and about the risks and the necessary precautions.

In some cases, particularly if you are in doubt over the answers to the following questions, you may need to consult your supplier or trade association or even obtain expert advice about what substances are involved in the work. Ask yourself if employees are liable to be exposed to hazardous substances in your workplace. Include service activities as well as production processes.

How can substances hazardous to health be identified?

- For substances brought in, check the safety information on the labels and the information for safe use provided by your suppliers (they are required by law to do this).
- Use your existing knowledge (eg past experience, knowledge of the process, understanding of current best practice in your industry, information on work related health problems in your industry).
- Ask your trade association and other employers in the same business for their experience and advice.
- Check COSHH: is the substance mentioned in any of the regulations or schedules? Is it listed in HSE Guidance Note EH40?

Question			
	Corrosives	**Acids**	**Solvents**
What is brought into the workplace? What is used, worked or stored? What substances are produced at the end of the work process?			

	Dust	**Fumes**	**Gases**	**Residues**
What is given off during any process or work activity?				

	YES	NO
Has the Health and Safety Commission approved an occupational exposure standard for the substances and is it listed in Guidance Note EH40/89?		
Is it listed in Part 1A of 'Information Approved for the Classification, Packaging and Labelling of Dangerous Substances' as being very toxic, toxic, harmful, corrosive or irritant?		
Is the substance present at a substantial concentration in the air?		
Is there a minimum exposure limit to the substance?		
Is it a micro-organism which can cause illness?		

(NB: If the answer is 'YES' to any of these questions, it may be a substance hazardous to health within the meaning of the COSHH Regulations. It depends on whether it arises out of or in connection with work under the employer's control.)

Figure 5.1   A typical COSHH preliminary checklist

- Examine published documentation, trade data, HSE guidance material.
- Check Part IA1 of the approved list issued under the Classification, Packaging and Labelling of Dangerous Substances Regulations 1984: anything listed as very toxic, toxic, corrosive, harmful or irritant comes under COSHH.

Do the ways in which each substance is handled or is present in the workplace give rise to any risks to health in practice now or in the future?

Observe, find out about and consider the following

- Where and in what circumstances are substances used, handled, generated, released etc. What happens to them in use?
- Is their form changed (eg solids reduced to dust by machining)? Identify places (eg handling departments, storage areas, transport).
- What are people doing; what might they do?
- What measures are currently taken to control exposure and to check on the effectiveness and use of those measures?
- Who will be affected (eg employees, employers, contractors, the public)?
- Is exposure liable to occur?
- Is it likely that some of the substance will be breathed in?
- Is it likely to be swallowed following contamination of fingers and/or clothing?
- Is it likely to cause skin contamination or be absorbed through the skin?
- Is it reasonably foreseeable that an accidental leakage, spill or discharge could occur (eg through breakdowns of the plant or control measures or operators' mistakes)?

Reach conclusions about people's exposure: who, under what circumstances, the length of time they are or could be exposed for, the amount they are exposed to, and how likely exposure is to occur. Combine this with knowledge about the potential of the substance for causing harm (ie its hazard) to reach conclusions about the risks from exposure.

Sometimes, of course, the quantities, the exposure time or the effects are such that the substances do not or could not constitute a risk – but you must have the information to back up this conclusion.

Action to be taken

If the assessment shows that there is no likelihood of a risk to health, the assessment is complete and no further precautions are needed.

If the assessment shows that further action is needed, you have to decide what needs to be done to complete the assessment requirements. If it is reasonably practicable to do so, you should prevent anyone from being exposed to any hazardous substances. Where it is not reasonably practicable to prevent people being exposed, you have to ensure that their exposure is adequately controlled and their health protected. In such cases you will need to:

- select the measures to achieve and sustain adequate control;

- work out arrangements to make sure those control measures are properly used and maintained;
- make sure your workforce is trained and instructed in the risks and the precautions to take, so that they can work safely. In some circumstances, employees need to be monitored and arrangements made for them to be under health surveillance (check COSHH and HSE guidance notes relevant to your work and trade literature).

Unless you can easily report and explain your conclusions at any time because the assessment is simple and obvious, you should make a record of it. Record or attach sufficient information to show why decisions about risks and precautions have been arrived at, and to make it clear to employees, engineers, managers etc what part they have to play in the precautions.

For example, if the conclusions alter the introduction of a new process or machine, or a change in the substances used, or if there is any reason to suspect that the assessment is no longer correct, the assessment must be reviewed to take account of these new circumstances.

PART 2

Welfare

Within the general terms of welfare it is necessary to provide sufficient and hygienic toilet and washing facilities in all places of work. There are additional requirements to provide washing facilities where the work is particularly dirty or arduous. These requirements will be found under the Factories Act 1961, the Offices, Shops and Railway Premises Act 1963 and the statutory instruments made under them. In addition, the HASAWA also requires that a safe and healthy working environment be provided and that adequate facilities and arrangements must be made for employees' welfare. This will include the provision of adequate and hygienic toilet and washing facilities.

All sanitary conveniences provided by an employer must be kept clean and there must be provision for lighting, ventilation and privacy. Where persons of different sex are employed, then proper and separate accommodation must be provided. There are rules concerning the number of conveniences outlined in the Sanitary Accommodation Regulations 1938 as amended in 1974. They are summarised in Table 5.11.

There is an obligation to provide and maintain proper washing facili-

Table 5.11 *A summary of the Sanitary Accommodation Regulations 1938 (Amended 1974)*

Minimum number of conveniences	
	Toilets
For every 25 female employees	1
For every 25 male employees	1
Where the number of males exceeds 100 and sufficient urinal facilities are also provided	4
For every 40 employees over 100	1
Where the number of males exceeds 500 then for every 60	1

(Note: In counting the number of employees, any odd numbers less than 25 or 40 is regarded as 25 or 40.)

ties, including the supply of hot and cold running water. In addition soap and clean towels (or hot air dryers) are also a requirement, and must be kept in a clean and accessible condition (see section 58(1) of the Factories Act 1961).

Alcohol and drugs

Alcohol has been identified as a contributory factor in a number of accidents in the workplace. It is important that workers are made aware of the dangers of drinking either before going to work or during it. Workers who drink heavily the night before may still be over the legal limit to drive a car the following day. It is unlikely that anyone unfit to drive a vehicle will be fit to operate machinery or equipment at work. An organisation must take steps to include in its policy on health and safety its stance over the use of alcohol and medicines. In cases of drinking alcohol personnel managers must consider:

● action to be taken in a one-off situation;
● action with a persistent offender.

In the case of the latter it may be possible to offer counselling advice, whereas the former might be easily dealt with under a disciplinary investigation, depending upon the circumstances. A similar system would be required where workers were found to be dependent on unprescribed drugs.

Workers who are taking prescribed drugs which medical practitioners have identified as being capable of clouding judgement or affecting manual dexterity should be afforded some protection, and light duties could be considered as an alternative in the short term. Workers should be encouraged to ask their general medical practitioners if any medicines that they have been prescribed will either effect their ability as a road user or as a worker.

Stress management

The ability to identify stress in workers must be encouraged. Being able to do something about it is the function of management. Stress has long been identified as a contributor to accidents, and it is therefore important that it is identified and dealt with. Stress can affect people in different ways. Stress can be eased by relaxing and building confidence, so the following are important:

● safety training;
● safety education;
● task analysis and the identification of areas of risk;
● bonus schemes and/or time management;
● inter-personal relationships;
● assertiveness;
● career and/or life planning;
● counselling;
● self-awareness;
● negotiation;
● team building;
● performance management.

However, stress management is best considered within the job profile and recruitment stages and these issues are developed further in other books in this series.

There have been attempts to quantify levels of stress and the example of the Holmes-Rahe scale of life change units (LCUs) is given in Table 5.12.

Cleaning

There is a requirement under the HASAWA for an employer to ensure a safe and healthy working environment. This will require premises to be kept clean and tidy. Most organisations subcontract this responsibility to office cleaning companies or undertake the task themselves. Office or factory cleaning usually takes place after everyone has gone home but, as the name implies, cleaning also includes good housekeeping while actually at work. Poor housekeeping is responsible for

Table 5.12 *Holmes-Rahe scale of life-change units*

Event	LCUs
Death of a spouse	100
Marital separation	65
Death of a close family relative	63
Personal injury or illness	53
Marriage	50
Loss of job	47
Marital reconciliation	45
Retirement	45
Change in health of a family member	44
Wife's pregnancy	40
Sex difficulties	39
Gain in family membership	39
Change in financial status	38
Death of a close friend	37
Job change	36
Argument with spouse	35
Taking out mortgage	31
Mortgage foreclosure	30
Change in working responsibilities	30
Sibling leaving home	29
Trouble with in-laws	29
Personal achievement	29
Spouse beginning/stopping work	29
Change in personal habits	24
Trouble with business superior	23
Change in work hours or conditions	20
Change in residence	20
Change in schools	20
Change in recreation	19
Change in social activities	18
Taking out a personal loan	17
Change in sleeping habits	16
Change in family social arrangements	15
Change in eating habits	15
Vacation	13
Minor violation of the law	11

more than half of all work accidents. People should not:

- block or litter walkways/gangways with raw materials or other 'essential' work items;
- carelessly discard food or liquids either over floors or equipment;
- throw or discard items around the work area which people can trip over;
- hang clothing on equipment not designed for the purpose;
- cover up important notices or signs;
- misuse waste containers;
- leave rest rooms and/or kitchen areas littered with motorcycle helmets and other equipment for people to fall over.

Hygiene

Employers should set out rules about the consumption of food and drink on the premises. Also, those organisations providing works canteens will be subject not only to the HASAWA but also the Food Act 1984 and those regulations made under it. It provides for:

- **injurious foods** in that it is an offence for any person to add any substance to food, use any substance as an ingredient in the preparation of food or subject food to any other process or treatment so as to render the food injurious to health, with the intent that the food be sold for human consumption in that state;
- **protection for purchasers** whereby it is an offence to sell to the prejudice of the purchaser any food which is not of the nature, substance or quality demanded by the purchaser.

It is also an offence to sell food which is unfit for human consumption under section 8(1) of the Food Act 1984.

Where food is kept or prepared, care should be taken to ensure that damaged sink units and refrigerators are well maintained. Personal hygiene should be monitored and provision made for washing and cleaning. Implements used for eating or drinking should not be washed in toilet areas and cracked sinks should be replaced as soon as possible.

CHECKLIST

- Are your fire procedures adequate?
- When was your last fire drill held?
- Does every employee know what to do in the event of a fire?
- Do your fire marshals know what to do when the fire alarm is sounded?
- Are you satisfied with your building evacuation times?
- Have you sufficient qualified first-aiders?
- Have you sufficient first-aid boxes and are they adequately stocked and checked?
- How often do you check building/room temperatures?
- Is your lighting adequate?
- Is your light bulb replacement programme satisfactory?
- Do you have adequate ventilation in accordance with current regulations and codes of practice?
- Are the current radiation requirements relevant to your working situation?
- What procedures do you have in respect of visual display units. For example, do you provide VDU filters and eye-sight checks for certain categories of worker?
- Are your protective clothing policies and procedures adequate?
- For manual handling purposes is your transport policy upheld and maintained?
- Are your storing and stacking guidelines up-to-date, appropriate and used satisfactorily?
- Do you have appropriate guidelines available for storing and lifting and are these adequate?
- When were your duties and responsibilities under COSHH last examined?
- Are your current procedures, policies and programmes adequate under the COSHH regulations?
- Are your current welfare facilities appropriate and adequate under the requirements of the law?
- Do you have a policy in respect of alcohol and drugs?
- Do your employees know of the dangers of alcohol and drugs and do they know how and where to get help?
- Are your management procedures capable of reducing/keeping stress to a minimum?
- Are your housekeeping and cleaning provision adequate?

CHAPTER 6
Accident Costs and Financial Matters

It is important that personnel managers have some understanding of management accounting, and in this chapter we start by considering financial management. We also cover how to cost an accident, budgetary control and economic rates of return.

Financial management considerations

Personnel managers should have a basic understanding of management accounting and its importance within the organisational structure. This will allow for decisions to be taken which provide for maximum safety for a known cost. All too often, safety related decisions are taken which later prove to be too expensive or do not provide an appropriate economic rate of return (ERR). Calculating an ERR will be discussed later in this chapter. Company accountants will need to know the financial implications of all safety management decisions, so it is necessary to spend some time looking at this issue together with current methods of estimating accident costs and the cost that these incidents can have upon the organisation.

Basically, financial management is a broad term applied to management accounting and funds management. Within the context of management accounting this concerns itself with information that is useful to management. It is defined as the application of accounting knowledge for the purpose of producing and of interpreting accounting and statistical information designed to help management in its functions of promoting maximum efficiency, and in formulating and co-ordinating future plans and measuring their execution. This form of accounting practice feeds off financial accounting, cost accounting, budgetary control and capital investment appraisal, but the emphasis is on the use of information to assist management to plan and control activities of the organisation rather than upon techniques. Funds management, on the other hand, concerns itself with the acquisition and control of funds; with sources of finance and the control of liquidity. As long-term planning proceeds, financial management must assess the implications of the policies proposed in terms of funds required and make arrangements to raise the long-term funds necessary to secure the financial foundations to provide for organisational growth. Short-term proposals are equally important. Irrespective of how big an organisation is and however profitable it might seem, it is still important to have the money available to pay the bills and the weekly wages. This emphasises the need to try to forecast future cash requirements both in the short and the long term.

Personnel managers need to know something about the techniques used to collect and summarise this information, but do not need the detailed knowledge that an accountant must have. This chapter discusses basic financial management concepts and does not intend to provide full coverage of a complex subject. Personnel staff wishing to learn more about the subject should consider the reading list given at the end of the chapter.

Costing an accident

Accidents cost an organisation considerable sums of money and justification for taking positive action within the organisation is based on this fact. As already discussed in Chapter 2, the aim of the personnel manager responsible for safety matters in his or her organisation will be to reduce accidents or prevent them from happening. Showing remedial strategies to be effective in meeting this aim will in turn save time, which can be simply translated into monetary terms. There are many methods for estimating the cost of an accident, but there are two classes of costs which result from an accident:

- costs from insurance (the insured costs); and
- uninsured costs.

In theory, an organisation can insure itself against any eventuality, but in practice the costs of doing this are prohibitive. Most companies, therefore, insure a part of their activities, such as those required by law, and accept liability for the remainder. For example, a worker who drops a casting on to the floor and breaks a toe will have compensation paid by insurance sources. The damage done to equipment or the casting itself may have to be borne by the company if such eventualities are not covered by insurance. Here are 10 elements connected with an incident which may be regarded as uninsured costs:

- cost of wages paid for working time lost by workers who were not injured but whose work output was interrupted by the accident taking place;
- the net cost to repair, replace, or straighten up materials or equipment damaged in an accident;
- cost of wages paid for working time lost by injured workers, other than workers' compensation payments;
- extra costs necessitated by the accident involving overtime work;
- cost of supervisors' wages while their time is required for activities necessitated by the accident;
- wage costs due to decreased output of injured worker after return to work;
- cost of learning period of any new worker employed during the injured worker's period of absence;
- uninsured medical costs borne by the company;
- cost of time spent on accident investigations and processing of HSE requirements and compensation type administration; and
- additional costs such as equipment replacement, hire or temporary facilities needed until normal state can be resumed, for example replacement vehicles involved in road traffic accidents.

A personnel manager must be in a position to calculate his or her company's accident costs and company accountants will usually agree the method to be adopted. A sample form used to extract cost data is given in Figures 6.1 and 6.2.

Such data will then allow a company to assess its own average accident costs, which vary from industry to industry, and this will provide for a better basis on which to assess budgetary requirements and improved programme evaluation strategies. It is easier to undertake prospective rather than retrospective studies, although organisations who do not do this may wish to undertake a small retrospective study in order to obtain a sample accident costing. In this case, remember that in order to help decide how many cases to look at or test the reliability of the averages, compute the standard errors of the averages. It is likely that a two-thirds fiducial probability will give an average for a dozen or more cases of a given type within one standard error of the true average for this type of case in your organisation. The standard

TAKING CARE OF SAFETY

Total time on light work — Hours Mins

Employees average percentage of normal output during this period — %

Where the injured employee was replaced by additional staff the wage cost for this period — £

Time the new employee was below normal for standard wage expected — £ Hours Mins

New employee's average percentage of expected (normal) output — %

New employee's hourly rate of pay — £

Time of supervisor in training new employee — £ Hours Mins

Medical cost to the organisation (not covered by employee's compensation insurance) — £

Cost of time by other clerical workers involved in processing accident paperwork — £

Other costs not detailed above (eg additional costs in renting equipment, public liability etc) — £

Total uninsured costs — £

Figure 6.1 Accident investigator's cost sheet

ABC Manufacturing Ltd

Accident Cost Report

Injury accident number ☐

Non-injury accident number ☐

Dangerous occurrence number ☐

Date ☐   Department ☐

Name of injured worker ☐   Works number ☐

(or name of worker reporting a dangerous occurrence)

Please answer the following questions:

1. How many other workers (not injured) lost time because they were talking, watching or helping at the accident? ☐

2. How much time did they lose? ☐☐ ☐☐

   Hours   Mins

3. How many other workers (not injured) lost time due to damaged equipment in the accident or required the output or assistance of the injured? ☐

4. How much time did most of them lose? ☐☐ ☐☐

   Hours   Mins

5. Describe the damage to materials and equipment:

   [ ]

6. Estimate the cost of the repair or replacement of the materials and equipment listed above £ ☐

7. How much time did injured worker lose on the day of injury for which he was paid? £ ☐

8. If operations (or machines) were stopped, will overtime be necessary to make up lost production? YES | NO

9. Will it be impossible to make up lost production? YES | NO

10. How much supervisor's time was used assisting, investigating, reporting, re-assigning work or instructing a substitute or making adjustments to work loads? ☐☐ ☐☐

    Hours   Mins

Name of supervisor ☐

Please pass this form as quickly as possible to the personnel manager/manager

Figure 6.2 A supervisor's accident cost report

ABC Manufacturing Ltd

Accident Cost Report

		Hours	Mins
Total lost time	(1)		
Treatment time	(2)		
First aid time	(3)		
Grand total (1+2+3)			

Name of employee [_____] Works number [_____]

Date of injury [___][___][___] Nature of injury [_____]

Department [_____] Operation [_____] Hourly rate £ [_____]

Average hourly rate in the department where the injury occurred £ [_____]

Wage cost of lost time by workers not injured (but by employer) £ [_____]

Number of workers who lost time because they were talking, watching, helping etc [_____]

Average time lost per worker [_____]

Number of workers affected by the accident or incident [_____]

Average time lost per worker [_____] Hours Mins

Nature of damage to equipment [_____]

Net cost to replace or repair damaged equipment £ [_____]

Wage cost of time lost by injured worker while being paid by employer (other than employees' compensation payments) £ [_____]

Time lost on the day of injury for which the employee was paid [_____] Hours Mins

Number of subsequent days absence for which the employee was paid [_____]

Length of shift or number of hours in standard day [_____] Hours Mins

Number of additional journeys for medical treatment in employer's time [_____]

Average time per journey [___] [___] Hours Mins Total [_____] Hours Mins

Additional lost time by employee for which he/she was paid [_____] Hours Mins

Lost production costs (include overtime extra supervision etc) £ [_____]

Cost of supervisor's time connected with the accident £ [_____]

Supervisor's time shown on report [___] [___] Hours Mins Additional supervisor's time required [_____] Hours Mins

Wages cost due to decrease in output of worker after injury (if rate paid) £ [_____]

error is equal to:

$$\frac{\bar{\sigma}}{\sqrt{N}}, \quad \text{and} \quad \bar{\sigma} = \sqrt{\frac{\Sigma x - \Sigma x \bar{x}}{N-1}}$$

N = number of cases
x = cost of an individual case
$\bar{x}$ = average cost

In a larger organisation it might be better to examine 25 to 30 cases.

Incentive schemes

There is evidence that some incentive schemes are a contributory factor in accidents. To take an example, the ABC Transportation Group paid its drivers on the number of delivery collections made during a working shift. The emphasis of the bonus scheme was on speed. It has been known for several years that speed is a major factor in accidents whether on the road or on the factory floor. In the case of the Bloggs Delivery Service a driver lost his life, 4 drivers were seriously injured and 11 were slightly injured in road accidents in one year. In addition to this, 37 per cent of the fleet of vehicles were damaged in some way during the same year. The cost of all this to the Bloggs Delivery Service was too much and the firm went out of business 18 months later. All incentive schemes involving drivers of vehicles should be based upon low accident involvement and low accident damage factors. For example, a driver completing one year of accident-free driving should be entitled to a minimum bonus based upon the savings in insurance premiums under similar conditions to the no-claims bonus operated by insurance companies. Some companies operate the RoSPA Safe Driving Award Scheme, but unless this is linked to a financial reward there is little incentive for drivers to take part. Careful recording of accident costs as discussed above should allow organisations to calculate meaningful schemes for their employees.

Payment by results

Some companies operate schemes based upon the number of items or actions produced within a certain time-scale. It is common for safety to be ignored from the processes involved unless the safety manager is consulted.

Incentive schemes give rise to much discussion, although this is as much due to the varying interpretations of what is meant by an incentive scheme and to the variety of opinion, as to what its objectives are. There are differences in the bases of assessment on which schemes are founded and also in the industrial atmosphere into which they must fit. Inevitably, there are good schemes and bad ones, and opinion of them is tempered by personal experience. Through job evaluation each job may be placed into a particular grade for which a specific remuneration is paid. For some jobs, this is all that is necessary in designing a wage payment system. Such a system is referred to as a time rate (TR) or day rate. Payment under such a system involves paying a person according to the time he or she spends at work rather than directly on the amount of work produced. There are sanctions on payment for work done. If no work is produced at all then it is unlikely that the person would be allowed to continue in the job! Alternatively, if the work done is excessive compared to what is expected, then some kind of reward (whether short term or in the long term) is usually received. The advantages of TR schemes are usually listed as follows:

- The employee has a guaranteed wage;
- wages are relatively easy to compute both by employee and employer;
- they provide low administrative costs;
- it is easier to control the quality of the work when wages are not dependent upon output;
- the wage system does not inhibit labour flexibility within a particular grade;
- day-to-day disputes over earnings are avoided.

The disadvantages of these schemes are that:

- there is no direct financial incentive to increase output;
- usually active supervision is necessary;
- productivity and therefore unit costs are impossible to forecast accurately.

One of the empirical rules upon which work measurement is based is related to the effort rating of a person working at standard performance. Under incentive conditions, this will normally be about one-third higher than the rating of a person working under non-incentive conditions. There can be no theoretical base for this rule. Its only justification is that it has been found to be generally true. From this, it follows that if one-third more effort is required to achieve standard performance from non-incentive performance, then incentive payment should be one third higher than non-incentive payment.

When the term *performance* is used, a comparison with one's concept of standard performance is implicit. Therefore to quantify performance, it is an expression of the standard time for a job (ie the time it will take at standard performance) as a percentage of the actual time in which the job was performed. This is shown as:

$$\text{Performance} = \frac{\text{Standard time}}{\text{Actual time}} \times 100$$

For example, if a person performs a job, the standard time for which is 10 minutes, in 8 minutes then his or her performance will be:

$$\frac{10}{8} \times 100 = 125\%$$

Many different schemes for payment by results (PBR) have been published in the 20th century. All such schemes do basically the same thing in that they relate performance to earnings in some way.

Calculating the safety factor

A number of incentive schemes have been discussed and so far no allowances have been made for the safety of the production process. It should be remembered that all accidents affect performance and thus produce a cost. Therefore, some means of including this within the calculations is necessary. Like incentive schemes generally, there are many methods of meeting this provision and most are based upon the number of reported accidents and dangerous occurrences carrying out specific tasks expressed as a proportion of the costs of those incidents. Some tasks will have a greater risk than others, therefore it will be difficult to calculate a standard rate to cover every eventuality.

Work measurement can be described as the application of techniques designed to establish the time for a qualified worker to carry out a specified job at a defined level of performance in *complete safety*. This poses three questions:

- What is a qualified worker?
- What is a specified job?
- What is a defined level of performance?

A qualified worker is one for which specifications have been established to define the job such as:

- the quality standard required;
- the method to be followed by the worker;
- the machines, materials and tooling to be used;
- the working conditions under which the job is performed.

Being a qualified worker means one who is accepted as having the necessary physical attributes, intelligence, skill, education and knowledge to perform the task to satisfactory standards of safety, quality and quantity. The term *performance* means a rate of working or alternatively a rate of output expressed as an average over the working day or shift.

There are two basic concepts regarding what levels of performance should be. These are:

- that it should be the level which can be reasonably expected under *motivation* conditions of employment; and
- that it should be of the level of performance which can be reasonably expected under *non-motivation* conditions.

The British Standard recommendation is that performance should be pitched at the motivation level. The term used to describe this level of performance is referred to as the *standard performance*. This is defined as:

the rate of output which qualified workers will achieve without over-exertion as an average over the working day provided they are motivated to apply themselves to their work.

It is not proposed to discuss the principles of objectivity, subjectivity or the general relevance of work measurement, but it should be remembered that the above definitions are not perfect and that work measurement has never pretended to be anything but an empirical discipline.

Facts rather than opinions are required to ensure effective planning and control of production. The *work value* of each job is one of the most important facts. The work value of a task consists of two factors. These are:

- the value of the sort of job; and
- the time required to complete the job.

The first is determined by:

- the market value of labour;
- agreements;
- legislation;
- job evaluation.

The second is determined by work measurement.

All organisations make some kind of estimate of the length of a job and there are three possibilities. These are:

- The use of a measuring technique which is systematic and has known, close limits of accuracy;
- guesswork;
- to assume that the time which is taken to do the job is the correct time.

The uses of work measurement are:

- *methods* to assess the relative importance of different parts of the method and to compare alternatives;
- *incentives* to provide a fair and realistic basis for incentive schemes;
- *machines* to determine machine loading;
- *men* to establish manning levels;
- *planning* to provide a basis for production planning;
- *control* to provide a basis for management control;
- *costing* to provide a basis for standard costing systems;
- *budgeting* to provide information for labour budgeting systems.

Although there are several uses listed above, work measurement is usually connected with establishing incentive schemes. This is why work measurement tends to be such an emotive subject. It must be pointed out that payment is only one use of time standards, although it is the most troublesome.

The majority of work measurement techniques involve the breaking down of the job to be studied into *elements*. For each of these elements, separate standard times are established. The standard time of the job as a whole is then the sum of all the standard times of its constituent elements. Standard times for these consist principally of three basic parts (although others may be added). These are:

- basic time;
- relaxation allowance; and
- safety factor.

Standard units of work

This should generally be broken down into the following:

- the quality of work in all kinds of jobs can be expressed in terms of the common unit;
- one work unit consists of three parts namely *work*, *relaxation* and *safety*;
- the proportion of each part varies with the type of job but the three parts together always add up to the common unit.

Work measurement uses five techniques which are:

- time study;
- synthesis from elemental data;
- predetermined motion–time systems;
- analytical estimating; and

- activity sampling.

These are discussed briefly below.

Time study
This is a method of recording the times and rates of working for the elements of a specified job conducted under specified conditions and for analysing the data in order to obtain the time necessary for the carrying out of the job at a defined level of performance. The times for the task are recorded using one or more stopwatches on the shop floor, which is largely why time study has met with and still does encounter opposition. Using the correct approach, however, resistance can usually be overcome.

Method study is a pre-requisite to time study, especially if the times obtained are to be used as a basis for incentive schemes. Time study also provides timings for separate work elements which can be used in synthesising times from elemental data.

SYNTHESIS FOR ELEMENTAL DATA
This technique is used to build up the time for a job at a defined level of performance by totalling element times obtained previously from time studies in other jobs containing either the elements concerned, or from synthetic data. When time elements recur in various jobs, the times may be recorded and filed so that when those elements occurred, records could be consulted for *all* the necessary elements and it is possible to compile a standard time without having to carry out a time study. This saves work and makes the compilation of standard times much faster and cheaper. When an attempt is made to time elements for synthesis purposes, elements have to be selected so that they have the widest application in the jobs which have to be timed. If the elements are too long and diverse, their field of application will be limited; and conversely if they are too short they may not be easily measurable.

PREDETERMINED MOTION–TIME SYSTEM (PMTS)
This is a system whereby times established for basic human motions (which are classified according to the nature of the motion and the condition under which it is made) are used to build up the time for a job at a defined level of performance.

ANALYTICAL ESTIMATING
This technique is a development of estimating whereby the time

---

required to carry out the elements of a job at a defined level of perform-ance is estimated from knowledge and experience of the elements con-cerned. Time study is mainly useful to analyse repetitive jobs, but is uneconomical to analyse non-repetitive work. On the other hand, a foreman's estimate or bargaining procedure are rarely satisfactory. Ana-lytical estimating is generally more accurate since it is systematic and based on the study of work. Time is not estimated for the job as a whole, but the task is first broken into elements as in time study, although in general, the elements tend to be longer. Times for these longer elements are worked out by a trained estimator. This technique is widely used to estimate times in engineering and construction work. Analytical estimating can give satisfactory results, although they will be less accurate than those obtained through time study or synthesis from elemental data. This method relies heavily upon the skill of the esti-mator who should be:

- trained in estimating;
- familiar with work study techniques;
- knowledgeable about the jobs for which he or she is estimating.

ACTIVITY SAMPLING

This method provides for a large number of instantaneous observations to be made over a period of time of a group of machines, processes or workers. Each observation records what is happening at that time and the percentage of observations recorded for a particular activity or delay is a measure of the percentage of time during which that activity or delay occurs. This is a statistical method which is based upon the same theory which underlies market research and opinion polls. This theory is that random observations can produce results whose accuracy depends on the number of observations made. This technique is used both in method study and in work measurement, and can also be used to quantify safety elements within a work unit.

More about time study

Of the five techniques of work measurement discussed above, it is advisable to examine time study in a little more detail for two reasons. First, because it is still the most used technique in practice and sec-ondly, because it contains some fundamental problems such as elements and rating. Time study procedure divides naturally into three stages which have been called:

- the preparatory stage;

- the study; and
- the concluding stage.

THE PREPARATORY STAGE

- Obtain the supervisor's confirmation that the job is ready for study;
- speak to the operator(s) to obtain co-operation or permission;
- observe the job as it is carried out and become familiar with it;
- check that safety regulations and standards are met;
- check that quality of standard of output is within specifications;
- check that job specifications are being adhered to and that method of doing the job is identical with agreements in force;
- check that materials being used conform to specifications;
- record the operator's name and other relevant information;
- sketch out details of any special aspects of the job;
- decide upon a suitable unit of production (this may be decided by company policy);
- break the job down into elements.

It is important to break down the job into elements because:

- a greater understanding of the job can be obtained if the job is analysed into elements;
- element breakdown is necessary as a basis for synthesis;
- rating accuracy is facilitated;
- allowance allocation is made more accurate.

There are three basic principles used as a guide to element breakdown. The selection of elements is often dictated by technical considerations. For example, if the elements are to provide a basis for future synthesis as well as being the constituent parts of an individual job, the choice of elements could well be based on the similarity between one job and another.

Principle 1 An element should be made up of one type of work only. That is:

- machine work should be separate from manual work;
- constant type work should be separate from variable work;
- work occurring in every work cycle should be separated from occasional work;
- heavy work should be separated from light work.

Principle 2 The end of an element should coincide with the natural break point in the work. If this can be identified by audible indications, then this will provide the observer with a relief from continuous observation.

Principle 3 The length of an element should be such that it aids accuracy in timing and rating. Opinions differ as to the minimum length of elements, but it is generally agreed that the shortest time in which an element can be rated and timed is about five seconds. The length of an element should be longer when:

- several comparatively short elements occur successively;
- the work is of such a scale as to make short elements unworkable.

THE STUDY

During a time study, each observed element is timed using a stopwatch and recorded on the study sheet. Simultaneously, each element is rated and the rating recorded. The rating is an assessment of the worker's rate relative to the observer's concept of the rate. This corresponds to the standard rating. The observer may take into account several factors necessary to do the job, such as speed of movement, dexterity, effort and consistency. Safety should also be seen to be included. Rating is carried out when elements are timed, since it is the assessment of the speed and effectiveness of the worker at that time. A work study observer must be conversant with the correct way of doing the job in order of reliability. Where safety is concerned, rating is probably the most important, albeit the most controversial, part of time study.

A work study observer must have some standard of rating to which he or she can relate his or her observations. In the past, it was assumed that the basis for this standard would be the output of the worker on time rates (datal rate or basic rate) and that a normal worker at incentive rate would produce one-third more in the same time. Of the many numerical rating scales in use, the most popular was the 60/80 or Bedeaux scale. This assumes that a normal worker will produce at a speed of 60 when on a time rate and at a speed of 80 when on an incentive rate. Other scales which are sometimes used are the 100/133 and 75/100 scale. More recently a 0/100 scale has been used, where the 100 corresponds with the 80 or 133 on the other scales but no lower point (60,100 on the other scales is defined (see Figure 6.3). Whichever system is used, it is necessary for safety practitioners to have an understanding of basic rating scales so that appropriate advice and input may be given.

THE CONCLUDING STAGE

Information gathered before and during the study is used to obtain the work content and standard time for the job. Basic time, sometimes referred to as extended, converted or standardised time, is defined as the time for carrying out an element of work at standard rating. This can be expressed as:

$$\text{Basic time} = \frac{\text{Observed time} \times \text{Observed rating}}{\text{Standard rating}} + 1\% \text{ for safety}$$

From the many observations of an element, a series of basic times are obtained. From these, the selected basic time for each element must be obtained. There are two basic methods of obtaining the selected basic time from a series of selected basic times, namely:

- the arithmetical mean method; and
- the frequency distribution method.

There are several allowances which may be applied to the basic time, depending on the circumstances. The main one is the relaxation allowance which is provided to allow a worker the opportunity to recover from the physiological and psychological effects of carrying out specified work under specified conditions and to cater for attention to personal needs. The amount of allowance depends upon the nature of the job. Other allowances permitted are:

- learner allowances;
- introductory allowances;

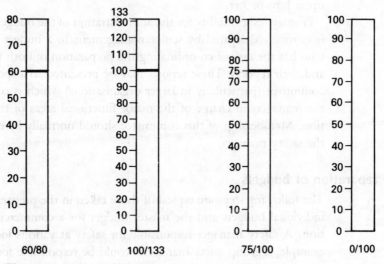

Figure 6.3 Safety rating scales

- contingency allowances;
- unusual conditions allowances;
- unoccupied time allowances;
- interference or synchronisation allowances.

Budgetary control

Most safety practitioners operate from a budget allocated to them for carrying out company safety policy. Having briefly discussed how cash is generated for such activities, it is now necessary to see how budgets should be controlled. A system of budgetary control establishes various budgets which set out in financial terms the responsibilities of management in relation to the requirements of the overall policy of the organisation. There should be a regular comparison of actual results with budget forecasts both to try and ensure (through action by the safety manager) that the objectives of safety policy are met and also to form a basis for any revision of such policy.

The crux of the budgetary process is that financial limits are allocated to component parts of the organisation. Thus, the safety manager plans activities in line with company policy and within the financial limits. It is important to try and obtain departmental management agreement to this financial limit as it is the manager who is going to be held responsible for keeping within it. Experience shows that a safety manager is more willing to accept responsibility for performance against his or her budget if he or she has been allowed to participate in the determination of the size of that budget, rather than it being imposed upon him or her.

Primary responsibility for the administration of the budgetary process is normally delegated by senior management to a budget accountant who has the task of co-ordinating the preparation of both the budgets and their reports. These reports may be presented to a special budget committee (particularly in larger organisations) which is composed of the managers in charge of the major functional areas of the organisation. Membership of this committee should normally be extended to the safety manager.

Preparation of budgets

The following steps are typical of those taken in the preparation of the individual budgets and the master budget for a commercial organisation. A safety manager responsible for safety at various locations, for example, a group safety manager, would be responsible for his or her own master budget, which would then form a part of the overall organisational master budget:

- a statement of overall safety objectives is prepared on which the individual budgets are to be based;
- forecasts are made regarding the general economic conditions and the conditions likely to be prevailing in the industry with accident data playing a key role;
- a safety budget can then be prepared based upon the forecasts and will highlight key task areas for action;
- a production budget is prepared in conjunction with the above and will require consideration of all materials and

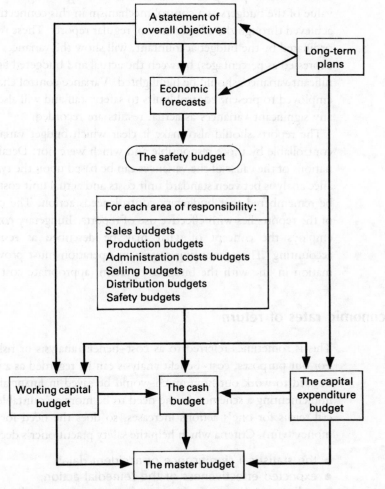

Figure 6.4 The preparation of the individual budgets and the master budget for a commercial organisation

other resources required to carry out the key task areas;
- the administrative cost budget is prepared for each area of activity;
- a capital expenditure budget covering anticipated changes in legislation, and detailing specialised equipment or modifications, is compiled.

The preparation of the budget is shown diagrammatically in Figure 6.4.

Budgetary control during the year

Once the year has started, the control aspect of the budgetary process consists of comparing the actual results to budgeted figures. The chief value of the budgets as a control mechanism in this connection will be achieved through the effective use of regular reports. These reports, co-ordinated by the budget accountant, will show the variances (normally expressed as percentages) between the actual and budgeted figures. Significant variances should be highlighted. Variance control charts can be employed to present control limits to safety staff and will also show up any significant variances as actual results are recorded.

The reports should also make it clear which budget variances were controllable by those responsible and which were not. Detailed explanations of the cause of the variances can be based upon the type of variance analysis between standard unit costs and actual unit costs. It must be remembered that budgetary control needs action. The chief value of the reports lies with effective use of reports. Budgetary control thus employs the concept of what may be described as responsibility accounting. The accounting system in operation must provide information in line with the budgetary system (appropriate cost centres).

Economic rates of return

This is sometimes referred to as cost–benefit analysis or risk analysis. For our purposes, cost–benefit analysis can be regarded as a procedure devised to work out how much would be saved in financial terms by implementing a scheme. As the need to be more accountable in financial terms for one's actions increases, so does the need for value for money (vfm). Criteria which help the safety practitioner's decisions are:

- the statistical significance of accident data;
- expected effectiveness of the remedial action;
- a discounted economic rate of return on expenditure;
- resource availability.

TAKING CARE OF SAFETY

The first two considerations are based upon an analysis of past accident records and the results of previous remedial measures undertaken.

The costing of human life is always very difficult but several attempts have been made in recent years to do this. Most consider the loss of working ability to society as a whole and in terms of emotional loss to a family. Whereas the first of these can be estimated fairly easily, given age, sex and social status of the person, the second has proved more difficult. When figures are given for the cost of an accident, there is usually a notional amount added for the emotional effects, but whether this is realistic or not is debatable. Whether someone dies on the road in a road accident or in the workplace, the results can be argued to be the same. Because of the severity of the road accident problems experienced by all nations, attempts have been made to cost such events. The same factors need to be considered in costing fatal, injury and non-injury accidents. Dangerous occurrences would need to be considered separately for each type of industry. In calculating the cost of accidents in the UK the following, which are based upon the cost of the number of elements averaged for each type of injury, are considered:

- the loss of output due to death or injury (loss of earnings plus non-wage payments);
- ambulance costs and the costs of medical treatment;
- the cost of pain, grief and suffering to the casualty, relatives and friends. Although considered to be important, the evaluation of these costs is difficult, so a notional figure is used in the estimated costs;
- cost of damage to property and equipment;
- cost of 'policing', administration and accident insurance costs.

Cost elements are re-estimated from time to time and in periods where no re-estimation is undertaken, costs are updated from those of the previous year using an index to reflect inflation and economic growth. This is carried out by multiplying the old cost by a factor equal to:

$$\frac{(1 + \% \text{ increase in prices})}{100} \times \frac{(1 + \% \text{ increase in GDP})}{100}$$

Although each industry (or organisation) can calculate its own costs based upon its own data, it is surprising that few actually do this. However, in the US many attempts have been made to cost accidents and to advise on appropriate benefits. For example, Figure 6.5 shows a risk–benefit analysis for comparing the cost of two methods of controlling asbestos pollution. The analysis shows that there would be a

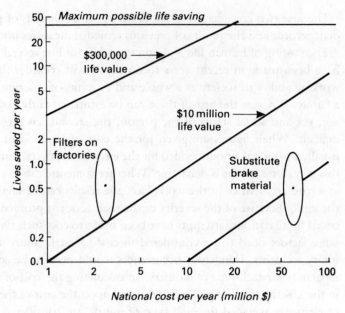

Source: American Industrial Hygiene Journal 4–77'Risk–Benefit Analysis for
Industrial and Social Needs' by Moll and Tihansky

Figure 6.5   Risk-benefit analysis

national cost of $10 million per life saved if filters were installed. Sub-
stitute brake materials would produce a cost of $100 million per life
saved. From this work, it was concluded that neither alternative comes
close to the $300,000 value that workers in hazardous occupations
implicitly give to their own lives. In the UK it is estimated that a life
is worth some £555,000, and an injury costs approximately £10,645.
The average cost of an injury accident, therefore, is £282,800. Accidents that only cause damage are estimated at approximately £650
(average), but this can vary from industry to industry.

When calculating the discounted economic rate of return of a
scheme, there are two factors to be considered:

● the capital cost of the scheme; and
● the benefits obtained over the life of the scheme computed
   at current value.

The capital cost will be a once-only payment, whereas the benefits
may take several years to accrue. When a scheme is chosen and capital
invested in it, other schemes cannot be implemented so there is a
resultant loss of potential benefit from them. This loss of benefit
reduces what is actually gained from the chosen scheme. The rate of
loss due to not spending the capital in another manner is called the

discount rate. Because prices may increase in the future, this rate is adjusted and is then referred to as the net discount rate. It is this latter rate that is always used in the calculations.

Benefits which cover the life of the scheme can be calculated if the likely first year saving or benefit (FYB) is known. The FYB(B) multiplied by the factor (V) from the net discount tables published by the Treasury will provide the expected total benefits. For example, if the benefit in the first year is £2,000, the life of the scheme is five years and the net discount rate is 7%, then the total benefit over five years will be:

$$£2000 \times 4.100 = £8,200 \text{ (where 4.1 is a multiplier calculated}$$
and issued by the Treasury via HMSO).

This is usually written as BV and is the benefit receivable over the full life of the scheme. The FYB(B) must take into account the net value of accident savings as well as any changes in maintenance costs and work times which are brought about by the scheme. So if:

A = accident savings
M = difference in maintenance costs
W = difference in work times

then B = A + M + W
and BV = (A + M + W) V

However, once the capital has been spent, it cannot be spent again, so the capital cost (C) must be subtracted from the benefits received to produce a net benefit over the life of the scheme expressed as a percentage of the original cost. The discounted economic rate of return is thus:

$$\frac{BV - C}{C} \times 100\%$$

Placing (B) in a different way into the above formula, the discounted economic rate of return is given by the following:

$$\frac{(A + M + W) - C}{C} \times 100\%$$

This is regarded as the basic formula for calculating cost–benefit analysis for the comparison of options.

Calculating local accident costs

In many cases, the proportion of accidents which are fatal and those which cause injury may differ significantly from those industry averages which are published from time to time. For example, the petroleum industry may publish figures as follows:

	Land based %	Off-shore %	Total %
Fatal accidents	36	64	100
Injury accidents	45	55	100
Dangerous occurrences	27	73	100

Most organisations only experience small numbers of accidents and in the absence of any other information it is better to use the average severity partition. However, if the number of accidents is sufficiently large to suggest a real divergence from average severity proportions, then the use of the average figures could lead to a serious under/over-valuation of likely accident savings. An indication as to whether this is appropriate can be obtained by calculating a range of values for estimated accident costs at the various in-house locations, so that if the range for the estimate based upon the severity proportions of accidents recorded lie outside the range using the average severity partition then there is a case for using the actual severity proportions. The following is a procedure used in the UK for estimating such ranges, but it must be acknowledged that this is not statistically rigorous but rather a convenient way to show whether there is a case for using local rather than group severity patterns. Using the average severity partition, a central estimate of total accident costs (T) is calculated thus:

$$T = C \times A$$

where

C = average cost per accident
A = number of accidents

The range of values for total costs is $T - s$ (Lower limit) and $T + s$ (Upper limit) where $s = C \times A$

A similar procedure is used to calculate a range of values for costs based upon the actual severity partition. The central figure for total cost is given as:

$$T = Cf \times Af + Ci \times Ai + Co \times Ao$$

and the value for s is given as:

$$s = Cf^2 \times Af + Ci^2 \times Ai + Co^2$$

where

>Cf = average cost of a fatal accident
>
>Ci = average cost of an injury accident
>
>Co = average cost of a dangerous occurrence (where damage occurred)

Research estimates that there are some 5.2 dangerous occurrences per injury accident, but these figures are based upon known occurrences and do not account for those which go unreported.

As before, the values of T range from T − s to T + s.

Calculating the time element

In addition to accident savings, remedial measures may produce changes in operating procedures either in a positive or negative way. This in turn will alter work timings. Although the purpose of remedial measures is the reduction of accidents, other effects can influence the rest of the work community, and these costs should be regarded as part of the cost of the remedial action and the current value of benefits adjusted accordingly.

CHAPTER 7
Safety Engineering and Mechanics

In this chapter we shall be looking at the following elements of safety engineering and mechanics: pressure systems/vessels, competent persons, lifting machinery and equipment, and electrical equipment. We shall finish by considering construction and building issues and examining maintenance procedures.

Pressure systems and vessels

On 1 July 1990, the Pressure Systems and Transportable Gas Containers Regulations 1989 came into effect. These regulations consider safety of pressure systems, not only at work, but places obligations of design and construction in respect of:

- design;
- manufacture;
- import;
- supply.

Pressure systems now require the provision of design information and appropriate markings. All such systems require correct installation so as not to give rise to danger. There are duties placed on employers regarding the competence and qualifications of persons who install and maintain such equipment.

A competent person is described as a person who must have certain attributes according to the complexity of the system and is an engineer of chartered or incorporated status (see below).

A personnel manager responsible for the management of health and safety should:

- know what pressure systems are installed at each premises;
- know what the safe operating limits are;

Table 7.1 *A brief summary of the pressure systems requirements*

Boiler with control systems requiring manual testing
A trained boiler attendant should be on site at all times when the boiler is in operation. Although the attendant need not supervise the boiler continuously, he/she should always be in a position where response to alarms can be carried out immediately. Previously it has been sufficient for an on-call boiler attendant to be available during the silent hours, who could be contacted from a permanently manned situation should an alarm sound.

Boiler with control systems which have automatic testing and self-monitoring
There should always be someone available on site who is competent to respond to alarms and to take appropriate action which at a minimum may be able to shut the boiler down safely before calling for the assistance of a trained boiler attendant. In practice, this would mean someone who has been trained to shut down the boiler in an emergency. These control systems should be checked on a daily basis by a trained boiler attendant except during weekends.

Pressure systems and transportable gas containers
The major difference between these new regulations and the old ones is a change in the classification of vessels which must be inspected and the requirement for the examination of some pipework. Examination and certification of vessels, pipework and protective devices forming a system or part of a system will have to comply with a written scheme of examination which has to be drawn up by a competent person, or certified as being suitable as a competent person.

Safe operating limits
The user of an installed system and owner of a mobile system shall not operate the system or allow it to be operated unless the safe operating limits of the system are established. The owner of a mobile system, if not the user of it, shall:

1. supply the user with a written statement specifying the safe operating limits of that system;
2. ensure that the system is legibly and durably marked with such safe operating limits and that such marks are clearly visible.

These regulations cover all situations and extend the requirements for routine periodic examination from steam plant and air receivers to every vessel or system which contains gaseous substances under pressure and hot water plant which contains water at a temperature above 111°C. Thus, not only are the boilers of such systems included but also the distribution of pipework and any heat exchangers or other devices where the water temperature exceeds 111°C.

- know where the inspection certificates are (either on the premises or at the insurers);
- know who the 'competent' person is;
- have a schedule of the pressure system drawn up (although this is not a legal necessity it is good management practice).

A system includes all associated pipe works, pressure parts and protective devices. The regulations apply in the following circumstances:

- where the company contains compressed gas (such as compressed air or liquified gas) at a pressure greater than 0.5 bar (approximately 7 psi) above atmospheric pressure;
- where there is steam where a pressure vessel exists and the plant is used by employees and/or self-employed persons.

A summary of the regulations is given in Table 7.1

Competent persons

Until the introduction of the pressure systems regulations, the term 'competent' had not been defined, but it is now accepted that a competent person is one who has such practical and theoretical knowledge and actual experience of the type of machinery or plant which he or she has to examine as will enable the detection of defects or weaknesses which it is the purpose of the examination to discover; and to assess their importance in relation to the strength and functions of the particular machinery or plant.

In law, a person may also mean a company, so it is quite acceptable for a competent person to mean a competent company. The following bodies may provide 'competent person' services:

- a self-employed person;
- a partnership of individuals;
- a user company with its own in-house inspection department;
- an inspection organisation providing such a service to clients.

It was important to clarify the meaning of a competent person because the HASAWA embodies the basic principle that an employer is generally responsible for the work activities of employees. When an owner or user procures another company to provide competent person services, the contract is not made with individual examiners but with their employer, who is ultimately responsible for their work. Statutory inspection reports are normally signed by the individual inspector on behalf of their employer. The duties of a competent person are to:

- advise the owner or user of a pressure system which is covered by the regulations of a written scheme of inspection;
- certify or compile written schemes of inspection;
- carry out inspections and assess future usage of the system.

Organisations specialising in providing advice on suitable competent persons are listed at the end of this book.

Lifting machinery and equipment

It is estimated that each year over 20,000 reportable injuries involve transport at work sites. Of these, about one-third involve lift-trucks. Not only do lift-trucks cause injury and death, they also damage equipment, goods being handled, buildings and fittings.

From accident investigation it is found that lift-truck accidents usually involve a driver or operator who has not received correct training. A personnel manager must, therefore ensure that all lift-truck drivers receive the following training:

- a basic course which provides the basic skills and knowledge necessary for safe operation, knowledge of the workplace and experience of any special needs and handling attachments;
- a specific course designed to give on-the-job experience under strict supervision.

Personnel managers arranging training should satisfy themselves that the training provided conforms to the Approved Code of Practice for the Training of Operators of Rider Operated Lift-Trucks. They should also ensure that instructors who are to provide this training are themselves qualified and that they only give training on lift-trucks which have been examined and certified. Instructors should also have a knowledge and understanding of the environment in which their trainees are to operate. All trainees should be tested in both the skills and knowledge required for safe operation. An employer should keep a record of each employee who has received training in accordance with the Code. An example of the form such a record should take is given in Figure 7.1.

Organisations accredited by the Health and Safety Commission to

Figure 7.1 Sample employer's training record

ABC Manufacturing Ltd

Employee training record

Employee's full name _____   Department _____

Employee reference number _____   NI number _____

Basic training

Lift truck types used in training

Model	Capacity	Attachments	Trained by	Course ref no.	Course date	Date of test

Specific job training

Model	Number	Instructed by	Tested by	Course date

Familiarisation training

Model	Capacity	Attachments	Trained by	Course ref no.	Course date	Date of test

Accident record

Date	Time	Location	Injury/non-injury	Details	Action taken

(Append statements, maps, drawings, costings and other accident detail to the record file.)

carry out lift-truck training in accordance with the Code are:

- Agricultural Training Board;
- Construction Industry Training Board;
- Road Transport Industries Training Board.

The addresses of these accredited training boards will be found at the end of this book under.

Electrical equipment

On 1 April 1990, the Electricity at Work Regulations 1989 came into effect. These regulations provide for the electrical safety of all areas while at work. The regulations describe:

- *an electrical system* as one where all electrical equipment shares a common source of electrical energy;
- *electrical equipment* as anything used or intended to be used to generate, control, distribute, use and anything else done with a supply of electricity.;
- *a circuit conductor* as anything capable of conducting electrical energy;
- *danger* as the risk of injury;
- *injury* as death or personal injury from electric shock, burn, fire, explosion or arcing initiated by and associated with electrical energy.

All electrical systems must be constructed and regularly maintained, so as to prevent injury or danger. In addition, all work activities at or near electrical installations must be carried out in a safe manner and safety equipment provided must be suitable for the purpose intended.

It is important that all electrical sockets, cables and electrical equipment are regularly checked and maintained by a qualified electrician. Care should be exercised when extension cables are used and advice sought where appropriate. It is the duty and responsibility of a safety manager to ensure that all technical aspects of health and safety are carried out by properly trained and qualified staff.

Construction and building issues

Construction and building sites are recognised as the most hazardous workplaces. According to published statistics, the construction industry employs under 10 per cent of the working population, yet provides 15 per cent of reported accidents and over 30 per cent of the fatalities. Site management is a specialist task and personnel managers with a responsibility for health and safety matters in the construction industry must seek appropriate advice and ensure that:

- the site manager is qualified to manage the health and safety requirements;
- appropriately qualified and trained staff are appointed;
- scaffolding, lifting gear and other apparatus conform to current codes of practice;
- resources are available for the provision of safety clothing and equipment where appropriate and that they are used correctly;
- a building site education and training programme is available;
- safety publicity is given a high priority.

There are a number of specialist consultancies and other related organisations which can provide a personnel manager with the appropriate advice on the safe and efficient running of a building site.

Working at heights is a hazardous part of the construction industry and it is usually human rather than equipment failure which is the major contributory factor in this type of accident. It is important, therefore, to ensure when workers are 'above ground' that:

- the right ladder is used;
- the ladder is set up correctly;
- appropriate ancillary equipment is set up correctly;
- equipment is inspected before use;
- ascents and descents are carried out correctly;
- weight capacities of the equipment are known and understood;
- all equipment is checked at the start of each working day;
- lifting gear engines are warmed up before use;
- clearance from electrical cables exists and is maintained;
- safety equipment is worn/used;
- high wind/wind-loading procedures are in place.

Where a personnel manager is involved in a construction-related task with subcontractors this checklist should be followed:

- list the name and address of the subcontractor;
- note the date and time of the meeting;
- list those people attending;
- provide details of safety policy, general site rules and permits to work to the subcontractors;
- obtain from subcontractors details of their safety policy, the names of their safety advisers (if any) and a method statement;

- identify areas where hazards might exist, agree what precautions must be taken and what work methods are to be used;
- agree codes of practice and standards;
- discuss what plant will be used and agree who will provide it, maintain it, inspect it and use it;
- liaise where necessary with trade union safety representatives;
- agree all necessary induction training/instruction for new employees and what specialist training is required.

Before work commences it is good practice to hold an initial on-site meeting where the checklist can be modified or updated as and where necessary.

Maintenance procedures

All machinery, safety clothing and equipment must be regularly maintained and inspected if they are to remain effective. Machinery safety has been highlighted more than any other area by enforcement, case law and civil liability. It is now accepted that the hazard-free machine cannot be produced, so it is a requirement to guard or fence machinery in such a way as to minimise the risk of injury to the worker or operator. Most case law, therefore, has tended to concentrate upon the guarding and fencing of machinery, rather than on the designers, manufacturers and suppliers of the equipment.

The following boundaries have been established by case law in relation to the guarding of machinery:

- only machinery which is in use has to be guarded or fenced;
- the purpose of guarding/fencing is to prevent employees and/or operators coming into contact with the machine;
- transmission machinery and prime movers are deemed to be dangerous, so statutory duties relating to them are considered absolute whereas other parts of the machinery are presumed to be safe unless shown to be hazardous;
- only machines used in the factory process are deemed to be machinery;
- mobile as well as static machinery are covered by statute;
- machinery, although guarded, may require fencing when working on material or where it is in close proximity to other machinery;
- hand-held tools are not regarded as machinery;
- there is no requirement to fence an unforeseen danger

created by the interaction of a moving part of a machine and a stationary object;

- if a machine is dangerous it must be fenced and putting up warning signs alone is not sufficient.

The Health and Safety Executive (HSE) have classified certain parts of machinery as dangerous and which should be securely fenced. The parts are:

- revolving shafts, mandrels, bars and spindles;
- in-running teeth between pairs of rotating parts such as gears;
- in-running nips of the belt and pulley sort such as those used in conveyor belts;
- projections on rotating parts;
- discontinuous rotating parts such as fan blades;
- revolving beaters, spiked cylinders and revolving drums;
- revolving mixer arms in casings such as dough mixers;
- revolving worms and spirals in casings, such as mincers or extruders;
- revolving high speed cages in casings, such as centrifuges;
- abrasive wheels;
- revolving cutting tools;
- reciprocating tools and dies such as power presses and drop stamps;
- reciprocating knives, blades and saws;
- closing nips between platten motions, such as printing machines;
- projecting belt fasteners and fast running belts;
- nips between connecting rods, rotating wheels, cranks and/or discs;
- traps arising from traversing carriages, such as metal planing machines.

While there is a vast amount of case law concerning dangerous machinery and lists provided by the HSE, it is also important for personnel managers to:

- identify dangerous machinery;
- ensure that dangerous machinery is guarded and/or fenced;
- ensure that employees are aware of the dangers;
- ensure that appropriate education, training and publicity is given to employees about these dangers;
- ensure that all guards/fences are regularly inspected and maintained in good working order.

A checklist for the safeguarding of machinery is given in Table 7.2.

Table 7.2 *Sample machine checklist*

Guards	Dangerous parts should be out of reach
	They should be strong enough for the purpose
	Fixed so as not easily removed
	Interlock the guard where necessary so the machine cannot start without the guard being in place
	Have a policy in respect of guards and publicise it to operators
	Seek specialist advice if in doubt
	Machines described as 'dangerous' may only be used by young people under strict supervision. Some examples are: guillotines, mixers, bacon and vegetable slicers, power wrappers and chain saws.
Check that	you know how to stop and start the machine
	all fixed guards and safety devices are fixed correctly
	all fixed guards and devices are properly working
	all materials to be used are clear of all mechanical working parts
	the areas around the machine are clear of obstruction and are neat and tidy
	in the event of the machine not working properly there is a recognised and known procedure for reporting and closing machines down
	appropriate safety clothing and equipment is being worn or used and is serviceable
	only trained and qualified staff use such machines

TAKING CARE OF SAFETY

CHECKLIST

- Have you listed all the equipment in use in your organisation which is subject to certain legal requirements?
- Have you obtained the various HSE and HSC advice notes concerning the machinery or equipment?
- Are you satisfied with your maintenance programme?
- Are you satisfied that guards and other safety devices are fitted, working and in use as required by company policy?
- Do you need to comply with the pressure systems and vessels regulations?
- Do you understand what a 'competent person' is and do you know how to seek their advice?
- Are you satisfied that all your electrical equipment, fittings and appliances conform to laid down safety guidelines?
- When did you last check that your duties and responsibilities described in this chapter are being carried out in a satisfactory manner?

CHAPTER 8
Safety Auditing

In this final chapter we ask the question what is safety auditing? We also cover safety policies, auditing safety procedures, practices and programmes, and finish by looking at safety audit management.

What is safety auditing?

There are many interpretations put forward about what exactly safety auditing is. Is it evaluation?, monitoring?, or research? Basically, safety auditing is a means of assessing performance in four areas:

- safety policy;
- safety programmes;
- safety practice;
- safety procedures.

To begin an examination of your performance you should start by answering the following questions which are typical of those asked in management audits. The questions may be listed under the four main heads listed in Figure 8.1.

Consider your activity in each of these areas over, say, the last 12 months, and answer these questions.

Inspections

- How many safety inspections have you made?
- How many unsafe conditions were found during these inspections?
- How many of these unsafe conditions were corrected as a result?
- How many unsafe behaviours were observed?
- How many of these behaviours were corrected?

TAKING CARE OF SAFETY

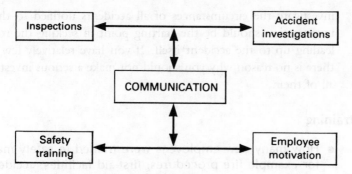

Figure 8.1 Safety performance appraisal

- How many unsafe conditions were reported to you?
- How many of these reports did you respond to?

Your answer to these questions will give some indication of your personal involvement in hazard spotting and correcting problems in the area for which you are responsible. You should be taking the lead in the supervision of safety and ensuring that your staff comply with the safety rules.

Inspections should be carried out frequently, how often really depends upon the magnitude of risk involved in the work. Safety representatives are entitled to carry out their own inspections and you should be prepared to respond to their reports appropriately.

Accident investigations

- How many accident investigations did you carry out (in relation to the number of accidents)?
- Were these investigations made promptly or were they made subsequent to an injury benefit claim or safety officer's enquiry?
- How many times did you discover the true cause of the accident? For example, if you ascribed the accident to operator error what factors such as training, supervision etc led to this error?
- How many causes could be attributed to failure in the management system?
- How many causes were remedied successfully?

Before choosing to investigate an accident a number of factors are generally taken into account such as the frequency of the occurrence, the severity of the injury, or just the unusual nature of the incident.

In fact there is a duty on all employers under the Social Security (Claims and Payments) Regulations 1979 to take reasonable steps to investigate the circumstances of all accidents notified to them. This investigation should be the starting point in seeking the root causes leading up to the accident itself. If you have relatively few accidents there is no reason why you should not make a serious investigation of all of them.

Safety training

- How many new employees were trained in safety matters, for example fire procedures, first-aid facilities, accident or hazard reporting, safety rules etc?
- How many existing employees have had refresher training in safety matters?
- How many safety briefing sessions have you given or arranged?
- How many of your staff have attended safety training courses?
- What improvements have resulted from this training?

If you found it difficult to answer these questions it may be because you have no tangible record of what has been done over the last year. It is important to keep a record of all training done, for without a record it will be very difficult to demonstrate compliance with the HASAWA.

Safety motivation

All managers will have a mission to make maximum effective and efficient use of resources with the maximum degree of health and safety. The concept of efficiency is seen as 'input centred', because it is concerned with ensuring that activities are carried out in the prescribed and appropriate fashion. Effectiveness, on the other hand, is seen as 'output centred' because it is concerned with the extent to which useful achievements are accomplished. An example list is provided in Table 8.1 where you are asked to consider whether the points listed are 'input' or 'output' centred.

The rationale underlying the need for personnel managers with a responsibility for health and safety to have a clear understanding of their objectives rests on a distinction that can be made between the concepts of efficiency and effectiveness. Effective managers:

- *do right things* rather than *do things right*
- *produce safe alternatives* rather than *accept tidy solutions*
- *optimise resource use* rather than *safeguard some resource*
- *get results* rather than *discharge duties*

Table 8.1 *Input or output exercise*

Topic	Input centred	Output centred
Internal safety audit (in your experience)		
Ensuring employees arrive/leave work on time		
Expecting tidy work areas		
Appraisal interviews		
Work study exercises		
Objective setting		
Safety budgetary control		
Accident reduction targets		
Expecting staff to be busy and hard working		
Expecting safety equipment/clothing to be worn		
Official personnel procedures		
Safety committee procedures		
Safety committee procedures		
The process of identifying safety training needs		
Safety management development courses		
Safety publicity exercises		
Internal safety campaigns (in your experience)		

While a manager might be regarded as efficient he or she might not be very effective when output results are measured. It is therefore necessary to set objectives so that areas of efficiency and effectiveness might be appraised within the framework of health and safety requirements, both voluntary and statutory. The consequences of not setting realistic objectives would be that an absence of goals will lead to input centred behaviour with role ambiguity and conflict being experienced.

Safety auditing, therefore, must examine objectives and the role of personnel within its policies, programmes, procedures and practices for efficiency and effectiveness.

Safety policies

Health and safety policies have already been discussed in Chapter 3, but policy documents held internally should also include an appendix which clearly outlines the aims and objectives for all staff. An example of the layout is given in Figure 8.2 and should include:

● an organisational mission statement;
● strategic objectives in relation to health and safety;
● tactical objectives;
● operational objectives.

ABC Manufacturing Ltd

Health and safety objectives summary

Mission statement

To reduce or prevent accidents from happening

(Insert your mission statement here)

Strategic objectives

To use a mixture of some or all of the following aspects of the safety mix efficiently and effectively

Safety education, training or publicity
Enforcement of safety requirements both statutory and voluntary
Environmental considerations
Applying appropriate safety engineering solutions to hazards

(Insert your strategic objectives here)

Tactical objectives

(List these here)

Operational objectives

(List these here)

Figure 8.2 A guide summary to safety objective setting

These *must* be measurable for safety auditing purposes. Resources allocated must also form part of the safety auditing process.

This aspect covers:

- legal requirements;
- statement of objectives;
- budgetary provision;
- staff;
- organisational structure.

It is also important to question whether the 'safety policy' is adequate.

This aspect covers:

- decision-making environment;
- safety committees;
- management involvement;
- trade union liaison;
- liaison with other interested groups.

Also considered in this section will be attempts to identify areas where difficulties are experienced for remedial action.

Auditing safety procedures

In this part of the safety auditing process, it is important to test that the administrative procedures currently in force are able to continue to implement organisational policy efficiently and effectively. Questions relating to this process concern the following issues:

- administrative structure;
- communication;
- time management;
- internal and public relations;
- recruitment;
- safety training;
- supervision;
- discipline.

Auditing safety practices

This covers those safety practices which may be based upon historical precedents or based upon professional ethics, codes of conduct and practice which directly involve organisational policy and procedure.

Questions regarding this concern:

- costing and valuation of accidents;
- accident investigation;
- data collection;
- medical examinations;
- welfare;
- hazard and risk assessment;
- accident analysis;
- equipment inspections;
- HSE Codes of Practice;
- professional codes of practice.

Auditing safety programmes

Here, the safety audit will examine past remedial strategies for efficiency and effectiveness and involves the four basic elements of the safety mix. These are:

- enforcement;
- engineering;
- environment;
- education.

A sample safety audit form is provided in Figure 8.3, but it must be pointed out that this document is purposely non-specific and is given simply to illustrate the sort of information which should make up the safety auditing process. There are commercial safety auditing packages available for those who wish to use them.

Safety audit management

It must be remembered that the aim of the safety audit or review is to improve organisational efficiency and effectiveness while its objectives are to reduce or prevent accidents from happening, to keep risk at a minimum, and the health and safety of the workforce at a maximum. For safety auditing to be effective it should be carried out by a person who has:

- some independence from all departments being audited;
- sufficient seniority and authority to carry out the task without hindrance;
- knowledge of health and safety statutory and voluntary requirements;
- ability to articulate findings to senior managers.

It must also be remembered that individuals and their roles within the organisation must also form an integral part of the safety auditing process. A light-hearted individual appraisal form is given in Table 8.2.

The framework for the individual personnel manager's health and safety objective setting is provided by a document known as the safety manager's guide. This differs from a job description in that it concentrates on the results the person is expected to achieve (outputs) rather than the activities he or she will undertake (inputs). The guide must identify the main purpose of the job's existence in the organisation, the key results that must be achieved to fulfil the main purpose, and the means by which one can assess whether these key results can be assessed.

At the end of an agreed timescale, the performance of individuals is reviewed against the results and targets contained in the safety manager's guide. In this way, the basis of the audit is performance rather than personality. Also, some relatively objective data is available in conducting the review. The safety manager's guide is, therefore, a document used to analyse the results which are expected of everyone in terms precise enough to be useful for safety auditing purposes. The safety manager's guide will consist of:

- main purpose of the job;
- key result areas;
- key tasks;
- standards of performance;
- control data;
- improvements.

Main purpose of job

This contains a brief statement of the reasons for the existence of the job within the organisation. It should not be a description or summary of the activities involved but should indicate the results or benefits that the job role contributes to the organisation. As a general rule, the main purpose statement should only include one verb, since to have more than one implies that the statement does not describe a single main purpose of the job.

In terms of health and safety a typical safety manager might state that the main purpose of his or her job is *to prevent accidents from happening*.

Key result areas

In every job, there will be a limited number of distinct areas in which effective performance makes a significant impact on the successful

Safety audit framework document

The following information is for internal use only. Responses to questions should not be accepted unless the reply can be substantiated.

---

1. Safety policy

Start the audit by examining the safety policy document in the following areas.

  i) Is it up to date?
 ii) Is any aspect of the document no longer relevant?
iii) How is the document distributed?
 iv) How is the information in it disseminated to employees?
  v) Who is responsible for the policy document?
 vi) Who is responsible for the way in which the policies have been formulated?
vii) What is the way in which future policies are to be made?
viii) Who is responsible for ensuring that the safety policy is implemented and evaluated?
 ix) When was the last time this exercise was carried out?
  x) List those persons who you have spoken to about this part of the safety audit.
 xi) List accident information and dangerous occurance detail.
xii) Outline the accident analysis programme and any changes.
xiii) Summarise the cost implications of accidents and dangerous occurrences since the last safety audit.
xiv) Were the policy recommendations from the previous safety audit implemented?
 xv) List those items which you are required to undertake by legislation and physically examine whether your organisation is fulfilling its obligations.
xvi) Examine key staff objectives for health and safety requirements.

Clearly itemise recommendations and conclusions from general comments.

2. Safety programmes

  i) How many safety programmes have been implemented since the last safety audit?
 ii) List the safety programmes carried out and obtain any evaluation data.
iii) Identify the relevance between the safety programme and the level and type of accident in the workplace.
 iv) Examine cost-effectiveness of safety programmes.
  v) List safety programmes by education, training and publicity and itemise literature used.
 vi) Comment on the value for money if external help was used.
vii) Obtain comments from key staff and from a random selection of other employees.
viii) Identify any areas where a shortfall in expectations or requirements have been noticed.
 ix) Identify recommendation not pursued from the previous safety audit.
  x) Examine staff appraisal forms for specific or specialised training needs.

Figure 8.3 Safety audit framework document

---

achievement of the job purpose. These are referred to as the key result areas.

A key result area is an area of work which is critical to the continued success of the main purpose of the job. Alternatively it is an area where, if the job were not done well, there should be a significant deterioration in the quality or quantity of work and results. One key result area for the safety manager might be *the safety training of all staff*.

---

3. Safety practices

   i) Itemise the way in which you collect and analyse accident and dangerous occurrence data.

  ii) Itemise the accident analysis process and additional information used.

 iii) Outline medical procedures and monitoring.

 iv) Outline welfare facilities.

  v) Outline hazard and risk assessment exercises.

 vi) Outline equipment inspection methods and frequencies.

 vii) List safety clothing issues.

viii) Examine HSE Codes of Practices where relevant and the way they are used and monitored.

 ix) Examine professional codes of practice and list these.

  x) List those practices which were identified at the last safety audit as being particularly hazardous and comment upon the changes (if any) made and their effectiveness.

4. Safety procedures

   i) Examine the administrative procedures for effectiveness in meeting health and safety objectives and company policy.

  ii) Examine communication systems for effectiveness in meeting health and safety objectives and company policy.

 iii) Examine time management procedures including work study requirements and bonus schemes.

 iv) Examine internal and external public relations procedures.

  v) Examine recruitment procedures and list those health and safety issues relevant to the recruitment process.

 vi) Comment upon safety training procedures.

 vii) Examine supervision procedures.

viii) Examine trade union contributions to health and safety matters.

 ix) Obtain the minutes of the Safety Committee since the last safety audit and examine recommendations and implementation.

  x) Examine discipline procedures for adequacy and relevance for health and safety.

5. Safety report

Ensure that the report outlines all findings and that recommendations are costed. Set these against the costs of non-implementation. Disseminate findings to key members of staff.

Table 8.2 *A light-hearted performance appraisal criteria for 'Supersafe' the personnel manager*

Performance Factors	Far exceeds job requirements	Exceeds job requirements	Meets job requirements	Needs some improvement	Does not meet requirements
Quality	Leaps tall obstructions with a single safe leap	Requires a running start	Can only jump obstructions without barbed wire	Crashes into obstructions but tries hard	Cannot recognise obstructions let alone jump
Timeliness	Is faster than a speeding train	Is as fast as a speeding train	Not as fast as a speeding train	Tries to keep up with British Rail	Runs into himself
Initiative	Is stronger than a bulldozer	Stronger than a bull elephant	Stronger than a bull	Smells like a bull	Is full of bull
Adaptability	Walks on water	Walks on water but only in desperate situations	Washes with water	Drinks water	Passes water in dangerous situations
Communication	Talks to God	Talks with saints	Talks to anyone	Talks to himself	Argues with himself but loses those arguments

Key tasks

Within each key result area one or more key tasks can be identified and defined in terms of specific actions and the results that those actions are purported to achieve. For example:

- to control...
- to plan...
- to determine...
- to develop..., and so on.

A key task might be *to ensure that the safety training budget is not overspent.*

Standards of performance

Identifying the effect of an activity assists to define the required level of performance and leads the way to transforming generalised statements of desirable objectives into specific targets against which success can be measured. Standards of performance are statements of the conditions that will exist when the results have been achieved satisfactorily. They should not be set at ideal, but rather at realistic levels. They must be feasible and be standards against which it is appropriate to judge the employee's performance. One key task may have several performance standards, such as:

- quantity – how many, how often?
- quality – how good, how safe?
- time – by when?
- cost – at what cost?

Wherever possible, performance standards should be measurable or objective terms. Some good examples of performance standards include:

- maintain all safety equipment;
- produce safety literature and advice free from errors in grammar, spelling and punctuation;
- to avoid overflowing rubbish bins;
- to keep safety equipment service time to not more than 10 per cent of working hours;
- to reduce safety maintenance to not more than 15 per cent of working hours from 20 per cent last year.

Some bad examples of performance standards are:

- to maintain safety equipment when requested;
- to maintain a high standard of English in safety literature;
- to empty waste bins twice a day;
- to keep safety equipment serviceable at all times;
- to reduce safety maintenance time.

When writing good objectives, an attempt should be made to include as many of the four elements of quality, quantity, cost and time as possible. It is unlikely that a meaningful objective would contain less than two of these elements.

Standards of performance in relation to the safety training (key result area) and financial control of the budget (key task) might be:

- information for the preparation of the annual health and safety budget obtained by [date] of each year;
- annual estimates prepared by [date] each year;
- financial control statements examined at the end of each accounting period in order to ensure that the estimates are revised immediately a new trend becomes apparent and that the difference between the actual expenditure and estimated expenditure does not exceed x per cent of the estimate or £y (whichever you have decided).

Control data

The next stage in the process is to identify the information that will be used to assess whether the performance standards are being met and also to identify the documentary sources that will be used to provide this information. This may be obtained from existing control documents, routine statistical information (such as accident data), reports and so on. Control data must be:

- accurate;
- available when needed;
- available in the right form.

The questions to be asked at this stage are as follows:

- Do you have sufficient feedback on progress in the system?
- Do you have continuous feedback concerning resource use?
- Have you ensured continuous comparison of performance?

In some instances, no adequate control data may be available. In these circumstances one must estimate the time it will take to obtain this information, then readjust the criteria accordingly.

Improvement of results

These are the recommendations for changes which are to be made from the safety audit in order that higher standards of performance in key areas are achieved. The types of action that these recommendations are intended to set in motion are:

- improvements in efficiency (resource use);
- changes in procedure or practice;
- further safety training, education or publicity;
- investigation into problem or high risk areas;
- action to improve or change organisational structure.

A safety auditor might ask questions like the following.

- What facets of the job cause the most problems, troubles, difficulties and accidents and what needs to be done and by whom, to bring about a worthwhile and lasting change?
- What is currently preventing higher standards being achieved?
- Would any of the work be simplified or made more safe if procedures or practice were altered, or another section or department did something different?
- What changes, if made, would make tasks easier or less risky to perform?
- Where could appreciable savings be made and how?

CHECKLIST

- Do you now understand the difference between safety auditing, evaluation, monitoring and reviewing?
- Are you satisfied with your current policy in respect of safety auditing?
- When was your last safety audit conducted and what happened as a result of it?
- Are you satisfied with your current safety policies?
- Do your current safety procedures need updating?
- Are you satisfied with your current safety programmes?
- Are your current safety practices in line with current codes of practice?
- Do you ensure that your safety auditor can conduct the exercise with complete independence?
- What do you do with the safety audit information which you have received?

APPENDIX 1
Table of Cases

Wilsons & Clyde Coal Co Ltd v. English ([1938] AC 57)

Donoghue v. Stevenson ([1932] AC 562).

Bourhill (or Hay) v. Young ([1943] AC 92))

King v. Phillips ([1953] 1 QB 429)

Doughty v. Turner Manufacturing Co. Ltd ([1964] 1 QB 518)

Rowark v. National Coal Board ([1986] unreported 86/45 CA)

Stokes v. Guest, Keen & Nettlefold (Bolts & Nuts) Ltd ([1968] 1 WLR 1776)

Davie v. New Merton Board Mills Ltd ([1959] AC 604)

Smith v. Scott Bowyers Ltd [(1986) IRLR 315]

Qualcast (Wolverhampton) Ltd v. Haynes [(1959) 2 All ER 38, HL]

Hudson v. Ridge Manufacturing ([1957] 2 QB 348)

Latimer v. AEC Ltd ([1953] AC 643)

Edwards v. NCB ([1949] 1 KB 704)

McWilliams (or Cummings) v. Sir William Arrol & Co ([1962] 1 WLR 295)

Paris v. Stepney Council ([1951] AC 367)

Smith v Leech Braine & Co Ltd ([1962] 2 QB 405)

Re Polemis v. Furness Withy & Co ([1921] 3 KB 560)

Overseas Tankship(UK) Ltd v. Morts Docks & Engineering Co Ltd ([1961] AC 388)

Wilson's and Clyde Coal Co v. English ([1938] AC 57)

Hudson v. Ridge Manufacturing Co Ltd ([1957] 2 QB 348)

Rushton v. Turner Bros Asbestos Co Ltd ([1959] 3 AER 517)

Scott v. Shepherd ([1773] 2 Wm BL 892)

Bowater v. Rowley Regis Corporation ([1944] KB 476)

Haynes v. Harwood ([1935] 1 KB 146)

Cutler v. United Dairies ([1933] 2 KB 297)

Sawyers v. Harlow UDC ([1958] 2 All ER 342)

Oliver v. Birmingham Bus Co ([1932] 1 KB 35)

Jones v. Boyce ([1816] 1 Starkie 493)

Woods v. Durable Suites ([1953] 1 WLR 857)

Glasgow Corporation v. Taylor ([1922] 1 AC 44)

Moloney v. Lambeth LBC ([1966] 64 LGR 440)

Wheat v. Lacon ([1966] AC 552)

Ellis v. Sheffield Gas Consumers Co ([1853] 2 E & B 767)

Tarry v. Ashton ([1876] 1 QBD 314)

Honeywill & Stein v. Larkin Bros ([1934] 1 KB 191)

Rylands v. Fletcher ([1868] LR 3 HL 330)

Woollins v. British Celanese ([1966] 110 SJ 686)

Regina v. Swan Hunter Shipbuilders Ltd ([1979] ICR 831)

Associated Dairies v. Hartley ([1979] 1 RLR 175)

Page v. Freight Hire (Tank Haulage) Ltd ([1981] IRLR 13)

APPENDIX 2
Useful Addresses

This section will include the name of the organisation, address and telephone number.

Centre for Health and Safety Studies
Department of Nursing Health and Community Studies
Bournemouth Polytechnic
Talbot Campus
Fern Barrow
Dorset BH12 5BB

Tel: 0202 524111

Royal Society for the Prevention of Accidents
Cannon House
The Priory Queensway
Birmingham B4 6BS

Tel: 021 200 2461

British Safety Council
National Safety Centre
62–64 Chancellor's Road
London W6 9RS

Tel: 071 741 1231 (10 lines)

Institution of Occupational Safety and Health
222 Uppingham Road
Leicester LE5 0QG

Tel: 0533 768424

Institute of Road Safety Officers
46 Apsley Street
Partick
Glasgow G11 7SW

Tel: 041 227 2048

Institute of Home Safety
132 North Road
Dartford DA1 3NB

Tel: 081 854 8888 ext 8086 (Secretary)

Royal Society of Health
RSH House
38A St George's Drive
London SW1V 4BH

Tel: 071 630 0121

Institute of Environmental Health
Chadwick House
Rushworth Street
London SE1 0QT

Tel: 071 928 6006

Institute of Occupational Hygiene
132 Oxgangs Road
Edinburgh EH10 7AZ

Tel: 031 445 1032

Health Education Authority
Hamilton House
Mabledon Place
London WC1H 9OX

Tel: 071 631 0930

British Standards Institute
2 Park Street
London W1 2BS

Tel: 071 629 9000

British Pest Control Association
3 St James' Court
Fire Gate
Derby DE1 1ZU

Tel: 0332 294288

Faculty of Occupational Medicine
Royal College of Physicians
St Andrew's Place
Regent's Park
London NW1 4LB

Tel: 071 487 3414

Royal Institute of Public Health and Hygiene
29 Portland Place
London W1N 4 DE

Tel 071 580 2731

Medical Commission on Accident Prevention
35–43 Lincoln's Inn Fields
London WC2A 3PN

Tel: 071 242 3176

British Medical Association
BMA House
Tavistock Square
London WC1H 9JR

Tel: 071 387 4499

Institute of Health Education
14 High Elms Road
Hale Barnes
Cheshire WA15 0HS

Tel: 061 980 8276/8696

Road Transport Industry Training Board
Capitol House
Empire Way
Wembley
Middlesex HA9 0NG

Tel: 081 902 8880

Construction Industry Training Board
Bircham Newton
Kings Lynn
Norfolk PE31 6RH

Tel: 0553 776677

Agricultural Training Board
Summit House
Glebe Way
West Wickham
Kent BR4 0RF

Tel: 081 777 9003

Health and Safety Executive
Daniel House
Trinity Road
Bootle
Merseyside L20 7HE

Tel: 051 951 4543

(for HSE also see your local area telephone directory)

The Data Appraisal Unit
Medical Division C5
Health and Safety Executive
Magdalen House
Stanley Precinct
Bootle
Merseyside L20 3QZ

Tel: 051 951 4000

The Chemicals Notification Unit
Central Directorate of Environmental Protection
Department of the Environment
Romney House
43 Marsham Street
London SW1P 3PY

Tel: 071 212 3434

Royal College of Nursing
20 Cavendish Square
London W1M 0AB

Tel: 071 409 3333

Further Reading

Chapter 1   Health and Safety Legislation

Dewis, M & Stranks, J, *Health and Safety at Work Handbook*, Tolley Publishing Co, 1988.

W Handley (Ed), *Industrial Safety Handbook (2nd Ed)*, McGraw-Hill, 1977.

Stranks, J & Dewis, M, *Health and Safety Practice*, Pitman Publishing, 1986.

Saunders, R & Wheeler, T, *Handbook of Safety Management*, Pitman Publishing, 1991.

R Howell & Barratt, *The Health and Safety at Work Act : A Guide for Managers*, B Barratt Institute of Personnel Management, 1975.

Selwyn, N, Selwyn's Law of Health and Safety at Work, Butterworths, 1982.

Smith, P (Ed), *Croner's Health and Safety at Work*, Croner Publications, 1989.

Spicer, R (Ed), *Croner's Health and Safety Case Law*, Croner Publications, 1990.

Wincup, M, *Modern Employment Law : A Guide to Job Security and Safety*, Heinemann, 1988.

Health and Safety Commission Leaflets

HASAWA
  HSC2 *The Health and Safety at Work Act 1974: The Act Outlined*
  HSC3 *The Health and Safety at Work Act 1974: Advice to Employers*
  HSC5 *The Health and Safety at Work Act 1974: Advice to Employees*
  Codes of Practice and Guidance Literature HSC11 Health and Safety at Work Act 1974: Your Obligations to Non-Employees

COSHH
  Control of Substances Hazardous to Health Regulations (1988): COSHH

Assessments: A step-by-step guide to assessment and the skills needed for it, HMSO, 1988.

Introducing COSHH: A Brief Guide for All Employers Introducing Assessment: A simplified Guide for Employers Hazard and Risk Explained, HMSO, 1988.

Chapter 2 The Role of the Personnel Manager

Manuele, Fred A, 'How Do You Know Your Hazard Control Programme Is Effective?' *Professional Safety* June 1981

RoSPA, *Health and Safety at Work Handbook* (3rd ed), Tolley Publishing Co Ltd, 1991

Saunders, R & Wheeler, T, *Handbook of Safety Management* Pitman Publishing, 1991

Croner, *Health and Safety at Work* Croner Publications, 1991

Arscott, P & Armstrong, M, *An employer's guide to health and safety management*, Kogan Page, 1982.

Bird, F & Loftus, R, *Loss control management*, RoSPA, 1984.

Perrow, C, *Normal Accidents*, Basic Books Inc, 1984.

Stone, R, *Management of Engineering Projects*, Macmillan Education, 1988.

BIM, *Managing Occupational Health and Safety*, BIM Management, Checklist No 91, British Institute of Management, 1990.

Chapter 3 Health and Safety Policy

HSC6, *Writing A Safety Policy Statement: Advice to Employers*, HMSO

HS(R)23, *A guide to the reporting of injuries, diseases, and dangerous occurrences*, HMSO

HSC7, *Safety representatives and safety committees*, HMSO

HS(G)48, *Human factors in industrial safety*, HMSO

HSE11, *Reporting an injury or dangerous occurrence*, HMSO

HSE17, *Reporting a case of disease*, HMSO

HSE, *The essentials of health and safety at work*, HMSO, 1990

Chapter 4 Accident Investigation

Clifford, B, *Eyewitness Testimony: Bridging of a Credibility Gap*, MacMillan Press, 1979.

Geiselman, R E, & Fisher, R P, *Interviewing Victims and Witness of Crime, Police*, Vol 7 March 1986 pp 26–34

Gregory, G, *Decision Analysis*, Pitman Publishing, 1988.

Loftus, E, *Eyewitness Testimony*, Harvard University Press, 1979.

Owen, F & Jones, R, *Statistics*, Pitman Publishing, 1990.

Greene, J & D'Oliveira, M, *Learning to use Statistical Tests in Psychology*, Open University Press, 1984.

Morris, C, *Quantitative Approaches in Business Studies*, Pitman Publishing, 1989.

Ferry, T, *Modern Accident Investigation and Analysis*, 2nd Edition, Wiley, 1988.

Farmer, D, *Classic Accidents: An Insight into Common Work Accidents*, Croner Publications, 1990.

Chapter 5 Occupational Hygiene and Health

Home Office, General Fire Precautions, HMSO, 1990

HSE, *Ventilation in the workplace*, Guidance note EH22, 1988

HSE, *Approved Code of Practice – Control of Substances Hazardous to Health*, 1989

HSE, *Essentials of Health and Safety at Work*, HMSO, 1990

HSE, *Noise at Work – Guidance on the Regulations*, HMSO, 1990

HSE, *Occupational exposure limits*, Guidance note EH40/90, HMSO, 1990

Croner's Health and Safety at Work, Croner Publications, 1991

Chapter 6 Accident Costs and Financial Matters

Beecham, B J, *Monetary Economics*, Pitman Publishing, 1988.

Morgan, P & Davies, N, *The cost of Occupational Accidents and Diseases in Gt. Britain*, Employment Gazette, London, HMSO, 1981.

Beardshaw, J, *Economics: A Students Guide*, Pitman Publishing, 1989.

Franks, J & Boyles, J, *Modern Managerial Finance*, Wiley, 1979.

Livesey, F, *Economics for Business Decisions*, Pitman Publishing, 1983.

Dalvi, M, *The value of life: A search for a consensus estimate*, HMSO, 1988.

Rosen, S, *Valuing health risk*, American Economic Review, 71(2) pp 241–245, 1981.

Jones–Lee, M, *The value of life and safety*, North Holland Publishing Co, 1982.

Jones–Lee, M, *The value of life and safety: a survey of recent developments*, The Geneva Papers on Risk and Insurance 10(36), pp 141–173, July, 1985.

Dickie, M & Gerking, S, *Benefits of reduced morbidity from air pollution*, Wyoming University Press, 1987.

Chapter 7 Safety Engineering and Mechanics

HSC, *Rider operated lift trucks – operator training*, HMSO, 1989

HSE, *Safe pressure systems*, IND(S)27(L), HMSO, 1990
HSE, *Competent persons*, IND(S)29(L), HMSO, 1990

Chapter 8   Safety Auditing

British Safety Council, *Safety Audit Checklist*, 1979.

Lees, F, *Loss prevention in the process industries*, Butterworths, 1980.

HASTAM, CHASE *Safety Auditing System*, Health and Safety Technology Ltd, Aston Science Park, Birmingham, 1991.

Index

abrasive 201
accessibility 121
accessible 124, 155, 163
accidental 31, 161
accidents 4, 6, 30, 32, 39, 43, 46, 48, 59, 62, 64, 65, 69, 74, 82, 84,
    101, 102, 112, 114, 115, 119, 120, 121, 127, 131, 132, 136, 139, 157,
    163, 164, 166, 169, 170, 174, 176, 187, 188, 189, 190, 191, 196, 198,
    205, 206, 210, 211, 216, 220, 226, 227
accident-free 174
accommodation 162
accountant 169, 184, 186
accountants 74, 168, 170
accounting 168, 186, 215
accused 29, 54
Acts 1, 4, 25, 27, 35, 47, 107, 111
administration 75, 76, 109, 170, 184, 187
administrative 54, 76, 119, 175, 186, 209
advertisements 71
advertising 228
adviser 45, 67, 155
advisers 199
advisory 27, 34, 53
agencies 59, 119
agency 39
agenda 67, 75, 76
agricultural 131, 198, 223
agriculture 27
aid 30, 31, 79, 110, 125, 138
air 46, 85, 119, 150, 152, 163, 195
airborne 152
alarm 45, 84, 142, 146, 167
alarms 142, 143
alcohol 59, 131, 138, 163, 167
ambulance 80, 148, 187
ankle 130
anti-slip 10

nurse 147
nursing 220, 224

obligation 11, 38, 44, 53, 63, 146, 162
obstruct 39, 41, 46
occupation 75, 103
occupational 25, 55, 147
occupier 20, 21, 22, 23, 25, 26, 48
offence 26, 29, 35, 40, 41, 42, 54, 106, 107, 166
offences 26, 33, 36, 39, 41, 53
offender 163
offices 27, 149, 159, 162
off-shore 27, 190
off-the-job 78
oil 7, 12, 14, 27, 120
operatives 43
operator 181, 196, 200, 205, 228
outdoor 130
overalls 8
overcrowding 26, 55
overflowing 215
overhanging 23
overtime 108, 170
oxygen 31, 32, 145

packaging 160
padding 158
pain 187
painful 6
pallets 158
paths 138
pay 47, 106, 110, 111, 169
payment 111, 174, 175, 176, 178, 188
pedestrians 157
penalties 40, 44
penalty 25
perception 75, 125
petroleum 189
physiological 183
plaintiffs 23
poisonous 21
policing 47, 187
political 108, 121, 122
pollutants 150
pollution 150, 152, 187
population 69, 198
preventative 7, 54
proactive 11, 60, 66
probability 12, 170
productivity 74, 110, 175

uninsured 169, 170
unions 30, 33, 101, 102
unlawful 23, 107
unoccupied 184
unreasonable 7, 9, 12, 40

vagueness 29
valid 8, 107, 112, 135, 147
vandalises 36
vaporising 142
vapour 14
vapours 159
VDU 155, 167
ventilated 143, 148, 150
ventilation 26, 27, 30, 120, 131, 150, 151, 162, 167, 227
vibration 55, 152, 153
vicarious liability 4, 15, 17
victim 137, 138
video 122
vision 155
visual 54, 123, 155, 167
volenti non fit injuria 18

wages 169, 170, 175
walkways 85, 158, 166
wardens 143
warning 21, 45, 46, 48, 115, 154, 201
washing 8, 20, 26, 30, 59, 162, 166
waste 6, 30, 85, 101, 143, 155, 166, 215
water 14, 25, 26, 36, 46, 85, 107, 142, 143, 145, 163
waterproof 10
waterproofs 156
watt 150
WC 221, 222
weather 120, 131, 138
welding 14, 31, 46
welfare 26, 27, 29, 30, 35, 36, 64, 101, 146, 162, 167, 210
wheelchair 148
witnesses 113, 119, 140
women 4, 55, 82, 107
workman 11, 16, 20
workmanship 22
workmen 11, 23
workplaces 34, 35, 136
works 45, 148, 166, 192, 195
workshops 12
worksite 22
workstation 126, 155

yards 14